EELS

A Biological Study

Silver eel nearly 3 ft. long on the first stage of its long journey from a small stream flowing into the Rhine to the Sargasso Sea in the western North Atlantic. It is making its way over a wet meadow, past seeding marsh marigolds, thus avoiding a mill.

Photograph by Ernst Zollinger.

EELS

A Biological Study

By the late

LÉON BERTIN

Professeur au Muséum
d' Histoire Naturelle
Paris

With 55 figures and 8 plates

LONDON
CLEAVER-HUME PRESS LTD.

CLEAVER-HUME PRESS LTD
31 Wright's Lane, Kensington
London, W.8

Translation by
BETTY ROQUERBE
revised and augmented
under the supervision of
MAURICE BURTON, D.Sc.
from the Second Edition of
LES ANGUILLES
(Payot, Paris)

First published
1956

*Printed in Great Britain at the St Ann's Press
Park Road, Altrincham*

Preface

UNTIL perhaps thirty years ago, one could reasonably speak of the *mysterious* life of the eel. Thanks above all to the marine expeditions and the researches of the great Danish biologist Johannes Schmidt, the central mystery of its breeding place, the problem which had intrigued and baffled observers down the centuries, had by then been finally elucidated. But the life cycle of the eel is none the less still a subject of the most intense interest, concerning which much remains to be clarified. And there can hardly in the whole of natural history be a more remarkable example of response to environment—to temperature, to salinity, to light and to current.

We can divide the life story of the European eel into eight phases : (1) Birth in the Sargasso Sea and existence as a transparent larva or *leptocephalus*. (2) Migration under the influence of ocean currents towards the Continental waters. (3) Metamorphosis of the leptocephali into minute transparent eels or *elvers*. (4) Invasion ("ascent") by these elvers of the Continental fresh waters. (5) Metamorphosis of the elvers into *yellow eels*. (6) Growth of these in rivers and lakes. (7) Final metamorphosis into *silver eels*, and the development of male or female sexual maturity. (8) Reproductory migration (or "descent") of the silver eels from the fresh waters to the ocean and hence to the Sargasso Sea where they breed and die.

The European eel is only exceptional because of the vast extent of its migration for thousands of miles across the Atlantic. All the many other species of eels accomplish the same kind of migrations in their lifetimes.

When we consider also the eel's exceptional resistance to changes in salinity, the toxic nature of its blood serum (which yet seems to be related to its capacity for surviving starvation, wounds and asphyxiation) and the fact that in early life male and female characteristics are not differentiated, we get some idea of the range and variety of the problems connected with this intriguing fish—many of them of interest to the layman as to the scientist.

Since the first edition of this book, much further work has been done on the subject. Ege and Jespersen, pupils of Schmidt, have used his immense body of findings to distinguish the species of intertropical eels; Bruun, another of his pupils, has managed, by injecting synthetic hormones into female eels, to bring them very near to sexual maturity. In Italy, D'Ancona has continued the study of juvenile hermaphroditism and the determination of sex; Fontaine in France and Koch in Belgium have studied the factors governing migration, such as the role of the endocrine glands. All this new material was incorporated in the second edition. For this English version some further additions have been made in the light of the most recent research, while the statistical treatment has been revised by Mr. D. W. Tucker to whom, as well as to Dr. Maurice Burton who supervised the translation, the author's thanks are due.

It is appropriate to dedicate this book to the memory of the illustrious Johannes Schmidt, to whom the author was personally indebted for so much advice and material for study. May it help to dispel the last obscurities attaching to one of the most famous biological puzzles of all time.

Paris, October 1955.   LEON BERTIN.

Publisher's Note. The death of Professor Bertin occurred while this book was in the press. An obituary notice by Dr. E. Trewavas will be found at the end of this volume.

CONTENTS

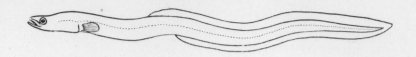

LIST OF PLATES

CHAPTER I

Pages of History

Truth and Legend

ARISTOTLE, it has often been said, committed the gross error of asserting that eels were generated from the earth's crust. Can we really believe this of one of the greatest philosophers and the most illustrious naturalist of ancient times, one whom we have been pleased to call the father of Zoology, Embryology and Physiology? Is the mistake in his original works or only in their translation? Let us re-read the passages in question. They are found in his *Historia Animalium and De Partibus Animalium.*

1. "*All fishes have seminal fluid or eggs. Eels have neither. Nobody has ever found one which, when dissected, showed the seminal canal or womb*". The first observation is correct; and it is true that the number of eels in which roe is seen is extremely small.

2. "*Some fishes leave the sea to go to the pools and rivers. The eel, on the contrary, leaves them to go down to the sea.*" It is a fact that silver eels migrate to the sea in autumn.

3. "*No eels are born from pairing or from eggs.*" This, we now know, is incorrect; and from the preceding facts, it would have been wiser to suspect that an eel does not become sexually mature nor reproduce until it reaches the sea.

4. "*After pools have been drained and cleaned of ooze, eels can be found re-forming themselves as soon as it rains.*" Today, we know that eels, with their strong resistance to desiccation and asphyxiation, can remain torpid in the mud at the bottoms of pools and become active again with the first rains.

5. Aristotle came, or at least seems to have come, to a more radical conclusion: "*The eels*", he said, "*come from what we*

call the entrails ἔντερα γῆσ *of the earth. These are found in
places where there is much rotting matter, such as in the sea,
where seaweeds accumulate, and in the rivers, at the water's
edge, for there, as the sun's heat develops, it induces putrefac-
tion."*

This essentially is the passage which suggested that Aristotle
believed in the spontaneous generation of eels. However, before
judging, let us look at a few more phrases which, though commonly disregarded, are nevertheless of the highest importance.
The first is this : " *As to animals, there are some which, like eels,
come from larvæ.*" The second defines what must be under-
stood by entrails of the earth : " *This substance in which the
bodies of the eels are found is of the nature of a larva.*"
Finally, Aristotle speaks of the eel as emerging, so to speak, from
a pupal stage: " *We have seen eels emerging from the skins
of these worms; and if one tears the worms apart and opens
them, one sees the eels clearly inside them.*"

Are we right, then, to translate the Greek expression
ἔντερα γῆσ by entrails of the earth? Ἔντερα, plural of
ἔντερον certainly means entrails or intestines, as in *enteritis*
and *mesentery*. But equally it describes earthworms, worms in
general and all vermiform animals. Aristotle may have meant
that eels were not born purely and simply from the mud,
or inert matter, but from worms or larvæ contained in it. These
worms, in their turn, could have been the elvers or very young
eels which we know ascend the rivers at the beginning of spring
and hide themselves effectively in the mud during the course of
the day. Thus, Aristotle may have known of the two principal
phases in the reproductive life of the eel: the exodus of the
adults to the sea, and the return of the young to fresh water.

Far inferior to Aristotle in knowledge, Pliny barely deserves
the title of naturalist. His *Natural History* is full of observations more or less correct, mixed indiscriminately with legends.
The truth emerges but fortuitously, as shown by the following
quotations about our present subject.

1. " It lives eight years." A method of saying, correctly,
that its growth is slow.

2. " It can stay six days out of water." A way of saying,
correctly, that it has a strong resistance to asphyxia.

3. " It goes every year, in prodigious numbers, to the sea "
—the autumn migration already observed by Aristotle.

4. " To reproduce themselves, the eels rub their bodies
against the rocks; from the shreds of skin thus detached come
new ones." At least, this idea is not absolutely silly. We propagate a begonia from a piece of leaf, and for Pliny, eels also
propagate themselves in a similar way.

According to Oppian of Sicily, contemporary of Marcus
Aurelius, the eel, or rather the Roman eel—the Ancients did not
make a distinction between them—became the bride of the
snake. One of the most moving passages in the *Halieutica*,
poems on fishing, is devoted to these unnatural loves. " Nothing
more is known ", writes Oppian " than what people repeat
about the loves of Roman eels and snakes. Some say that they
pair, that, full of eagerness, drunk with desire, the Roman eel
comes out of the sea to go and meet her mate. Urged by de-
vouring passion, the odious lustful snake goes crawling to the
water's edge. Seeing a hole in a rock, he vomits his fatal poison;
he empties his teeth entirely, clearing them of the black, perni-
cious fluid with which they are armed to kill; for, flying to his
love, he wishes only to be gracious and amiable. Arriving on the
beach, he stops, and intones his whistling love song. As soon as
she hears his voice, quicker than an arrow, the black Roman eel
darts towards the shore while the snake throws himself into the
sea foam, and swims to meet her. Their mutual desire is satis-
fied. They are together. Panting with pleasure, the female
draws the snake's head into her mouth."

And here is the result of this meeting : " Their passion satis-
fied, the one returns to her element, the other with long undula-
tions regains terra firma. There, he re-absorbs the black poison
which he had previously ejected. But if sometimes a passer by,
having recognised the fatal liquid, has thrown it into the water,
then, in desperation, the snake bangs his head against the stones
until he dies. He cannot outlive his shame."

I know of countrymen who, though not in such colourful
terms, tell of having witnessed by night the mating of the eel
and the grass-snake. Since the first are capable of leaving the
pools and the second of entering the water, it needs only a short

stretch of the imagination to conclude from this that they are searching for one another to mate.

After Oppian, who lived in the second century, nothing is to be gained by reference to writers of the Middle Ages who merely repeated without criticism the old ideas. Equally, renaissance learning yields us nothing. None of the great artists or scholars of the 15th or the 16th century studied eels. Da Vinci and Palissy, who did so much for the exact interpretation of so many phenomena, are silent on the subject.

In the 17th century, a great figure arose beyond the Alps: that of Francesco Redi, a gentleman of Tuscany, writer, poet, author of distinguished letters. The third volume of his writings contains his scientific works, one of them, written in 1684, called *Degli Animali viventi negli Animali viventi*, Animals living in living Animals—one of the first treatises on parasitology. Studying the parasitic worms of fishes, Redi was led to study eels, and what he says is contained in a few remarkably concise lines:

" I can affirm, following my long observations, that each year, with the first August rains and by night when it is most dark and cloudy, the eels begin to descend from the lakes and rivers in compact groups, towards the sea. Here the female lays her eggs from which, after a variable time depending on the rigours of the sea, hatch elvers or young eels which then ascend the fresh waters by way of the estuaries. Their journey begins at about the end of January or the beginning of February and finishes generally at about the end of April. It is not accomplished all at once but at intervals. The number of elvers is such that fishermen whom I asked to fish the waters in between two bridges over the Arno, in the town of Pisa, in 1667, took in five hours and using only sieves, more than 3,000 pounds.[1] Another fisherman, also in the Arno, and without going further than half a mile from the sea, caught at daybreak more than 200 pounds. They were so small and thin that it took about 1,000 to weigh a pound. However, it must not be thought that they are all the same size; the big ones are very few in number and the majority are small."

[1] A Tuscany pound was about 0·9 lb. (0·4 kg.)

It would be difficult to express in better terms the three manifest phases of the reproduction of eels : the migration of the
adults towards the sea, the spawning in the sea; and the return
of the elvers into fresh water. Further discoveries could not
invalidate but only supplement these observations.

Of course, in his treatise on parasitology Redi was preoccupied with the so-called viviparity of eels—the belief that
their young were born fully developed. He had no difficulty in
showing that the little animals found in their bodies were nothing but parasitic worms. " The worms of the eel, seen under
the microscope, are formed like a cone, at the bottom of which
is found the head. Out of the head, one sees protruding a horn
or trunk which can be retracted, whose surface is made thorny
by a great number of little points that cover it." One need be
only slightly familiar with the classification of the parasitic
worms to recognise in this description Nemathelminths of the
genus *Echinorhynchus.*

Although the belief in the viviparity of the eel was refuted
by Redi, it was perpetuated in later scientific writings. Leeuwenhoek, in 1692, described the bladder of the eel as its womb and
the worms found in it as young eels ready to be born. Linnæus
made the same mistake in the 18th century, in the successive
editions of his *Systema Naturæ: "anguilla"* he observes, *"parit
vivipara."*

In 1800, in his *Histoire Naturelle des Poissons*, Lacépède was
still more explicit : " The eel comes from a true egg, as all fishes
do, but this egg hatches more often than not in its mother's belly
. . . pressure on its lower part facilitates the issue of the young."
And to crown this, Lacépède warns against the false science of
certain naturalists inclined to be content with hasty and incomplete observations. He criticises Aristotle, Pliny, Leeuwenhoek
and even Spallanzani, of whose sound and honest judgment, on
the contrary, we shall learn more presently.

The tenacious belief in the viviparity of the eel rests not only
on the confusion between a parasitic worm and a foetus, but
also on the confusion between the eel and another truly viviparous fish of northern Europe, *Zoarces viviparus,* in which
the female brings into the world, each year, hundreds of young.
The *Zoarces* does not very much resemble an eel; its body is less

elongated and it possesses pelvic fins placed, it is true, under the throat and relatively invisible. It is a fish of the blenny family. This does not stop the fisherman of the Baltic and the North Sea from calling it *Aalmutter,* mother of the eels.

DISCOVERY OF THE FEMALE ORGANS

Despite the general survey by Redi, many points in the history of eels still remained obscure. The genital organs, notably, remained undiscovered despite all research, until Mondini, professor at the University of Bologna, suddenly announced their discovery in the female eel. His *De Anguillæ Ovariis,* published in 1777, is a masterpiece of precise description, in which the organs, considered both together and separately, are figured in a remarkable plan (plate II). The ovaries are ' frilled ribbons ', meaning that they resemble the collars and ruffs of former times. They extend dorsally all along the abdominal cavity and finish at a point a short distance behind the anus. The left ovary is longer than the right.

In these frilled organs, previously considered as adipose fringes, Mondini observed ova which he compared with those of the conger and the Roman eel; no doubt could remain of their identity. The ovaries of the eel are very often called for that reason ' organs of Mondini '.

The 18th century can be regarded as the golden age in the development of natural history. People were not then, as to-day, distracted by news from all over the world, but delighted to study at home or abroad all the marvels offered to human curiosity. Linnæus in his garden at Uppsala laid the foundations for a classification of plants. Buffon at Montbard, or in the *Jardin du Roi,* found new and original things to say on the more common animals. More especially, the traveller who knew how to observe found the most sensational discoveries at every step.

Lazare Spallanzani is an example. Professor of Natural History at the University of Pavia, in 1788, he made a voyage to the ' Two Sicilies ', as Sicily and the Kingdom of Naples were called; he also visited the Island of Elba, the Apennines, and went on to Venice. The chapters in the narrative of his journey, are surprising in their variety : *Journey to Vesuvius;* " *The Dog's Grotto* "; *Etna; Stromboli; Researches on the Origin of Basalt; Phosphorescent Medusæ observed at Messina; The Coral Fishery; In Search of Swordfish,* etc.

We must not forget that Spallanzani was also a very illustrious physiologist. To him is owed the first artificial digestion and a refutation of the theory of the spontaneous generation of the Infusoria. It is not surprising that he made studies on eels. The chapters concerning them have for a general title *Essay on the natural history of eels in the lagoon of Comacchio.* [See fig. 29]. The points dealt with are four in number :

Spallanzani confirmed Redi's observations on the entry of young eels into fresh water and the migration of the adults to the sea. After asking himself whether the eel reproduced in fresh water or in the sea, and after discussing the arguments for and against, Spallanzani concluded in the following terms. " For myself, if I am permitted to offer advice in this controversy, I suggest that reproduction in eels is really effected in the sea. The constant efforts, made at definite times, by the eels of Lake Comacchio, to escape from their prison, this persistence in trying to surmount all the obstacles they meet, this obstinacy in letting themselves be caught rather than turn back, all these movements of a blind instinct which carries them to a sojourn in the sea as soon as they are fully grown, can only result from a need as lively as it is imperative, and what need more pressing, more irresistible than that of the propagation of their species?"

Spallanzani approached the problem of viviparity, examined the so-called embryos found—unexpectedly— in the ' bowel ' of some eels, and concluded, like Redi, that these are nothing more than parasitic worms.

Is the eel then oviparous? No one has ever found an eel carrying eggs : " In the space of 40 years," writes Spallanzani, " the quantity of eels opened at Comacchio for the salting trade has been at least 3,400,000 *rubi* [1] to which must be added those consumed by the fishermen, which can be put at 400,000 rubi, these men having nothing else for food. Now if, as we may reasonably suppose, a *rubio* of eels contains on an average 40 individuals, we shall have a total of 152,000,000 eels of which not one has been found pregnant when opened."

[1] The *rubio,* a measure of capacity, was in N. Italy about 8·25 litres.

Yet Mondini claimed to have seen ovaries which he described under the name of ' frilled organs '. Spallanzani re-examined these organs, and globules which might have been eggs. He extracted them, and submitted them to various tests. His conclusions were doubtful. Perhaps they were eggs, but there was no absolute proof of this. According to Pasteur, Spallanzani was certainly " one of the most able physiologists with whom science had been honoured, the most ingenious and the most difficult to satisfy ".

Must we lose hope? Let us listen again to Spallanzani : "This problem, far from discouraging us, must excite our utmost efforts. If Aristotle has vainly attempted to investigate the secrets of nature, if Leeuwenhoek and Vallisneri [1] have worked in vain, if Mondini has only left one doubtful discovery, the way of experience and observation is always open to their successors ".

DISCOVERY OF THE MALE ORGANS

His successors have, in fact, answered the hope expressed by Spallanzani. The male organs were first discovered in 1874. A Polish naturalist, Syrski, Director of the Museum at Trieste, announced it under the title " Uber die Reproductions-organe der Aale " in the *Sitzungsberichte der Akademie der Wissenschaften* at Vienna. His great triumph was to have searched for the testes, not in the biggest eels, as had instinctively been done hitherto, but in those of medium size. The males are, in fact, smaller than the females and never grow to more than 20 inches in length. It is not possible to confuse the testes and the ovaries in the adult eel and the two are never found in the same animal. The testes occupy the same position as the ovaries, but instead of being like the ' frilled ribbons' of the latter, they are looped or festooned.

To tell the truth, the nature of a reproductive organ can only be determined by the presence in it of ova or spermatozoa. Syrski had only observed granulated heaps separated by thick partitions. What value then, in the face of this negative fact,

---

1 Vallisneri, a physician of Padua, had described the swim-bladder of the eel as an ovary.

are conclusions based purely on anatomy? That is the question that for many years preoccupied the most celebrated and leading anatomists and histologists at the end of the 19th century. Professor Claus of Vienna, Siebold of Munich and Virchov of Berlin, directed the work of their laboratories on to it. All these efforts were in vain. One of the more assiduous searchers, Freud, a pupil of Claus, published his results in a memoir, modestly entitled: " Observations on the form and the fine structure of the looped organs of the eel, organs considered as testes ". He claimed to have observed only problematic cells, which were perhaps, but not certainly, the mother-cells of the spermatozoa. This work is dated 1877. It must be agreed that the testes eluded scientific investigation longer than did the ovaries and still their true nature was not revealed. Yet the solution of the problem was at hand. By 1880, in fact, the German scientist Hermes, observed in the aquaria of Frankfurt and Berlin conger eels in a state of sexual maturity. Their testes, similar to the looped organs, were full of soft roe. Thus, the complex problem of the common eel was found to be linked with that of the conger, which was easier to solve. Hermes published a series of notes, which were immediately translated into many languages, making known from year to year the progress achieved.

Everywhere, new researches were beginning. Finally the looped organs were shown to be truly young testes: small sinuous spermatic canals, ramifying and anastomosing, embedded in a web of conjunctive tissue and themselves surrounded by a layer of cells which are the mother-cells of the spermatozoa.

It now remained for these last to be examined. This was accomplished in 1897, when Grassi and Calandruccio had the good fortune to capture in the sea, in the Straits of Messina, the first sexually mature male eel. This discovery was followed by another, in 1903, when Feddersen found in a Danish fjord a second eel with testes full of spermatozoa (Plate V).

DISCOVERY OF THE METAMORPHOSIS

At the same time as the mystery of the reproductive organs was being probed, the eel delivered up to the naturalists another of its secrets: that of its larval form.

B

It was in 1856, in his " Catalogue of the Apodes " that the German naturalist Kaup described for the first time the larva of an eel. This larva, from the Straits of Messina, was for many years in the collections of the Paris Museum, but unfortunately, it is no longer there. All my efforts to find it again have been in vain. Those figured here (plate VII) were photographed much later by Schmidt. It must be admitted that they do not look at all like eels. Kaup considered them to represent a new genus and species of fishes, which he called *Leptocephalus brevirostris*. The name leptocephalus has been used since to describe all larvæ which, like this one, have the appearance of transparent leaves.

Forty years later, in 1896, two Italian scientists, Grassi and Calandruccio, working in the laboratories at Messina, obtained proof that *Leptocephalus brevirostris* is the larva of an eel.

All discovery is a matter of chance and luck. That of the metamorphosis of the eel could not have been accomplished so easily elsewhere than in the Straits of Messina. These straits separate Sicily from Calabria, and form a plateau under the sea bounded to the north and to the south by depths ranging from 1,000 to 2,000 metres. Every year, on the equinoctial tides, the straits are the scene of violent conflicting currents on this plateau, causing an upsurge. This explains why animals living normally at great depths are thrown up on the beaches of Messina and of Torre del Faro. Among these, leptocephali are found in great numbers. Others are found in the stomachs of sun-fishes (*Mola*).

Because of this manna of leptocephali Grassi and Calandruccio were first able to establish, in 1893, the anatomical identity of the leptocephalus and the eel. Above all, two arguments helped them in this demonstration :

1.—The average number of muscle segments in *Leptocephalus brevirostris*—which is 115—is equal to the number of vertebræ in the eel. Now, we know the relation which exists, in all vertebrates, between the muscles and the vertebral column. To each half vertebra there is a corresponding half muscle segment and *vice versa*. To have established this parity between the leptocephalus and the eel is sufficient to be able to presume a relationship between them.

2.—All bony fishes have, at the end of the vertebral column, hypural bones which support the rays of the caudal fin. Those of the leptocephalus are exactly comparable to a rough draft of the hypural bones of the eel and have exactly the same number of rays (Fig. 42).

The identity is continued in the pectoral fins, the branchiostegal rays supporting the opercular membranes, in the disposition of the nostrils, the form and structure of the digestive tube, kidneys, etc. " The entire organisation of the *Leptocephalus brevirostris* corresponds to that of the common eel if we make allowances for the kinds of changes seen in the metamorphosis in other species ".

The anatomical comparison repeated by Facciola, in 1894, did not, however, carry conviction. It was always possible to suppose that chance alone was the cause of the resemblance between the leptocephalus and the eel. A suggestion put forward in turn by Günther (1880) and Belloti (1883) was that leptocephali must be regarded as monstrous larvæ incapable of continuing their development.

So it came about that, in 1896, a first-class discovery was made. There appeared, at intervals of a few months, two sensational notes in the *Reports of the Royal Academy of Rome* in which Grassi and Calandruccio announced that they had, on the one hand, watched in an aquarium the metamorphosis of the leptocephalus into the eel, and on the other had caught in the sea a metamorphosed form or semilarva.

THE DISCOVERY OF THE SPAWNING GROUND

Thus the eel certainly reproduces in the sea since its young form is a marine larva. The hypothesis of Redi and of Spallanzani had been confirmed. Only one point still remained obscure. Where are the leptocephali born? Where do eels reproduce? We shall see how this new problem was resolved in the 20th century by the illustrious Danish oceanographer and biologist Johannes Schmidt. (Plate I.)

We must follow year by year his discoveries which extend from 1904 to 1922.

In 1904, a Danish ocean-research ship, the *Thor*, was carrying out researches on the reproduction of the principal fishes used for food in northern Europe. Using a fine-meshed trawl, eggs and larvæ of cod, herring, whiting, plaice, etc., were obtained. Among these larvæ was found one day, around the Faroes, a leptocephalus measuring 77 mm long. It was the first leptocephalus to be captured outside the Straits of Messina. This capture was of the highest interest to the young and promising oceanographer, Johannes Schmidt, and decided him in accepting from the Danish Government the arduous task of discovering the spawning ground of the eel. " I had then," he wrote later, " only a slight idea of the extraordinary difficulties offered by this problem . . . The task grew from year to year to an unimaginable degree. In fact, it necessitated cruises of investigation from America to Egypt and from Iceland to the Cape Verde Islands ". (Fig. I.)

In 1905, the second oceanographic expedition of the *Thor*, intentionally directed farther south, obtained leptocephali not in ones but in many hundreds. Their length ranged from 70 to 80 mm. Their digestive tube was empty, showing that they were not taking any more food and that they had reached their full growth. A few months later, the *Thor* took some in the process of metamorphosis.

It is important to note that all these larvæ and semi-larvæ were found around the coasts and more precisely at depths of less than 1,000 metres. None could be found in the Channel, North Sea, or, more especially, in the Baltic. It could only be concluded that *eels reproduce in the open ocean*.

In 1906, the third expedition of the *Thor* was made around the Bay of Biscay. Hundreds of leptocephali were taken once again in waters over the great depths. This does not mean that they live in deep waters. During the day, they are at a depth of a hundred metres and during the night at about 30 metres. They are, as we say, pelagic larvæ (πέλαγος high sea).

In 1907, there were no fresh cruises. Schmidt devoted this enforced rest to the study of many thousands of European eels. He demonstrated that all belong to one species only. There was no evidence of local races or geographical varieties. There is no need to remark on the importance of this discovery.

If the eels were of different breeds, this would be the proof

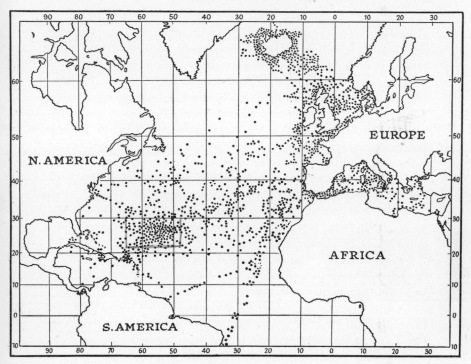

FIG. 1. The search for the breeding-place of the European eel. Stations of the *Thor, Margrethe, Dana* and other Danish ships between 1904 and 1922 (*after Schmidt*).

that they reproduced in different places. Their specific identity, on the contrary, favours the presumption that they have but one spawning ground, situated somewhere in the Atlantic.

From 1908 to 1910, the *Thor* made many cruises in the Mediterranean, which she traversed in all directions using the best fishing equipment that could be devised. Schmidt made two big discoveries:

1.—The Mediterranean contains only larger leptocephali, of which the smallest are 60 mm. long.

2.—These leptocephali become bigger and bigger from west to east, from the Straits of Gibraltar to the eastern Mediterranean.

Schmidt concluded with good reason that all these leptocephali are immigrants from the Atlantic via the Straits of Gibraltar. The Italian, Greek, Egyptian, Tunisian, Algerian eels do not reproduce in the Mediterranean, but go, as do all the others, into the Atlantic Ocean for their spawning.

This called forth a general protest from the Italian naturalists. Grassi, in particular, strongly attacked what he considered to be a big mistake. If Schmidt, he thought, has not found very young leptocephali in the Mediterranean, it is because he has not searched properly or the numbers of his hauls are insufficient. But how could this explain why this same method of fishing had obtained immense numbers of eggs and larvæ of all the other species of the Mediterranean fishes?

Grassi did not attempt to settle this contradiction. One senses in him an obvious determination to prove that Italian eels cannot be reproduced anywhere except in Italian waters: " I have already," said he, " called attention to the inadequacy of a thesis according to which *our* eel would not really be *ours* but would have originated in the Atlantic Ocean ".

Despite everything, proofs continued to accumulate in favour of an exclusively oceanic reproduction. The cruise of the *Thor* in the Mediterranean had just finished when a Norwegian ship, the *Michael Sars*, took in the neighbourhood of the Azores about twenty leptocephali, smaller and younger than any taken previously. They measured from 40 to 60 mm. Their intestines were full of food, and other circumstances of their capture showed that they were about one year from the time of their metamorphosis. Their presence off the Azores pointed to a spawning ground to the south-west in the Atlantic.

Rapid progress in the discovery of this spawning ground would have necessitated at that time a research ship with a wider range of action than the *Thor*. Lacking such a ship, Schmidt made an appeal to the goodwill of all masters of ships. From 1911 to 1915, 23 ships of Danish nationality cast their nets more than 500 times. In this way, yet younger and younger leptocephali were collected.

In 1913, the schooner *Margrethe* having been put at his disposal, Schmidt was able to go from the Faroes to the Azores, from there to Newfoundland and finally to the West Indies where the ship sank. The crew and the collections were saved and among the collections were 700 leptocephali of which the smallest were only 10 mm. in length. Their capture in the Sargasso Sea indicated that there was the spawning ground. However, Schmidt was scrupulous not to announce it yet. It was only after the war, in 1920, having had put at his disposal a powerful ocean-going ship, the *Dana,* that he completed his magnificent discovery.

The spawning ground of the European eel, surprising as it seems, is located in the neighbourhood of the American coast between 22° and 30° latitude north and between 48° and 65° longitude west.

From this area, the larvæ or leptocephali are carried towards Europe by currents, their journey lasting $2\frac{1}{2}$ years. As the shallower waters, surrounding the Continent of Europe, are approached these same larvæ metamorphose into young transparent eels or elvers which invade the littoral lagoons and the rivers.

Thus, the outstanding dates in the elucidation of the natural history of the eel are as follows :

350 B.C., Aristotle established that eels migrate to the sea and suspected, perhaps, the ascent of young eels into fresh water.

1684, Redi observed the exodus of adult eels and the return of the young. He propounded the hypothesis of spawning grounds in the sea.

1777, Mondini discovered the ovaries or " frilled organs ".

1856, Kaup described the *Leptocephalus brevirostris,* but without imagining it could be the larva of an eel.

1874, Syrski discovered the testes or looped organs.

1896, Grassi and Calandruccio observed the metamorphosis of the leptocephalus.

1922, Schmidt discovered the spawning ground in the Sargasso Sea, and brought to an end a problem of more than two millennia.

CHAPTER II

The European Eel

Characteristics and Variations

"To be able to study the biology of a species of fish with any certainty we must have exact information regarding its systematic position."

"So far as the freshwater Eels (*Anguilla*) are concerned, we still lack the necessary presuppositions for a certain classification, not only in regard to the numerous outside species, but even to our European freshwater Eel. Here, in fact, we have opinion against opinion without at the moment control or confirmation. Until the validity of the characters used in distinguishing the species has been tested by a detailed examination, we can neither characterise our Eel by contrasting it with other races in systematic regards nor draw the lines of its distribution."

So writes Johannes Schmidt at the beginning of his researches on eels.

In this spirit, we must deal first with the characteristics of the eel, then with the variations in these characteristics. Finally, comparing the eel, a migratory fish, with a completely sedentary species, such as *Zoarces viviparus,* one of the Blennies, we can shed a particularly revealing light on its life-cycle.

WHAT IS AN EEL?

In modern classification, the European eel forms part of the class Fishes, of the sub-class Osteichthyes, or bony fishes, of the order Apodes, and of the family Anguillidæ, of which it constitutes the single genus *Anguilla*. As these terms are rather obscure to the non-specialist we had better explain them briefly.

That the eel is a fish, nobody doubts. An aquatic vertebrate with a variable temperature, and breathing throughout life by means of gills, it possesses the three principal attributes of its class. Being referred to the Osteichthyes means that it is capable of producing bony tissue and that its paired fins have the axial skeleton short with fin-rays, on the contrary, strongly developed.

The order Apodes is composed of fishes that are elongated and snake-like, and are without pelvic fins. Their unpaired fins form a swimming fringe more or less continuous along the back and tail. Their scales are rudimentary or absent. There is no distinct premaxillary bone in the upper jaw, a character that distinguishes them from other fishes lacking pelvic fins, but which are not true Apodes in our sense of the word, such as the reed-fishes (*Calamoichthys*), sand-eels, pipe-fishes etc. Among the Apodes, the family Anguillidæ is distinguished by the possession of both pectoral fins and scales.

Let us examine an eel. Its elongated subcylindrical body is not really snake-like, although it resembles, in the lateral compression of the tail, certain species of sea-snakes. It is called more precisely *anguilliform,* as are the greater part of the Apodes.

Like all fishes, the eel is composed of a head, trunk and tail. The posterior limit of the head (Fig. 2) is indicated by the gill openings, which are narrow, and by the insertion of the pectoral

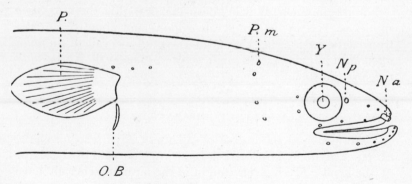

FIG. 2. Head of an eel.

Na, anterior nostril; *Np*, posterior nostril; *O.B.*, gill opening; *P*, pectoral fin; *Pm*, mucus pores; *Y*, eye.

fins. The anterior limit of the tail is marked by the anus which is found a little forward of the middle of the body.

The unpaired fin is continuous and has no fewer than 500 rays, extending from the last third of its back round to the anus after passing round the end of the tail. It combines the dorsal, anal, and caudal fins. This last cannot be distinguished except by an anatomical study of the bony parts or hypurals, which serve to support its rays (Fig. 42).

On the head of the eel, we can distinguish, from behind forwards, the gill openings, the eyes, the posterior nostrils in the form of simple holes, the anterior tubular nostrils situated on the front end of the snout, and finally, the mouth which extends as a long slit back under the eyes. Mucus pores are distributed at various points.

It will be noted that the lower lip projects as compared with the upper lip, the reverse of what we find in the conger, a marine eel of a different family. In addition the conger (genus *Conger*) is also distinguished from the eel (genus *Anguilla*) by its skin being entirely without scales and by its dorsal fin beginning far back.

In the eel's mouth are numerous, sharply-pointed teeth (cardiform teeth) inserted in the jaws (maxillary teeth), and in the middle of the palate (vomerine teeth). We shall see later on the important part played by these teeth in distinguishing the numerous species of the genus *Anguilla*.

For the moment, it will suffice to know that there are five species of eels in the temperate regions and about ten in the tropical regions. The European eel must be called *Anguilla anguilla* (Linnæus), although some authors call it *Anguilla vulgaris* Turton.

VARIABLE CHARACTERS

Fishermen and naturalists of all times have recognised the existence of many kinds of eels by their colour and by the shape of the head. The big eels caught in the autumn generally have brilliant and contrasting colours, which the ordinary eels do not have. Their black backs contrast with their coppery flanks and especially with the brilliant white underparts. These are called

Silver Eels, and are the sexually-mature individuals taken in the course of their migration towards the Sargasso Sea.

The eels which are not silvery are called Yellow Eels, or more picturesquely, *anguilles de genêt* (" broom eels "). Fishermen also distinguish a dark and a light variety, the intensity of colour depending upon the depth at which the animal is living. These yellow eels are sexually-immature and their whole activity is devoted to feeding. The Italians call them *pasciuti*, grazing-animals, in contrast to Silver Eels, which always have empty stomachs.

Eels are divided according to the shape of the head into broad-nosed and sharp-nosed eels (Fig. 3). The first have a short muzzle, blunt, and more or less depressed; the second have

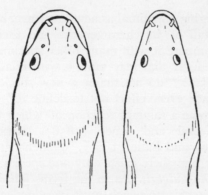

Fig. 3. Heads of a broad-nosed and of a sharp-nosed eel.

the muzzle long and narrow. In the broad-nosed eel, the eyes and nostrils are placed wider apart and the lower lip is more pronounced than in the sharp-nosed kind. Physiologically, the former is distinguished from the latter by its slower growth and by the more considerable size it can attain in the course of a longer existence.

Already known to the Ancients, these facts were first systematically set forth by Risso in the *Histoire naturelle de l'Europe méridionale* (1826). This author gave the two kinds the scientific names of *Anguilla latirostris* and *Anguilla acuti-rostris* which other scientists, including Ekström (1835) have translated into *Anguilla platyrhina* and *Anguilla oxyrhina*. The detailed observation of a large number of eels enabled Risso to add an intermediate kind, which serves to connect the two extreme forms.

Cuvier (1829) divided the form *latirostris* into *plat bec* and *pimperneau* which he equated with the English grig eel and glut eel. Yarrell (1836), however, regarded grig and glut eel as alternative names for the broad-nosed eel.

Kaup (1856) defined no fewer than fifteen species or pseudo-species; every difference in colour, in the proportions of the body, etc. distinguished for him a new one. In the Paris Museum is a collection containing all Kaup's types and it is sufficient to examine them to see how much his classification lacks foundation.

Before considering an animal as new to science, it is well to be informed in detail of its characteristics and their degree of variability, to compare it with many other specimens, to try to discover intermediates that may unite it with related forms. In brief, one may say : " do not define a new species unless you have already made every effort not to define it."

After Kaup came a salutary reaction of which the principal authors are Heckel and Kner (1858), Siebold (1863), Blanchard (1866) and Fatio (1890). Blanchard, above all, is categorical. For him there exists only one species, which must be called *Anguilla vulgaris*. As to the forms *latirostris, medio-rostris* and *acutirostris*, to which must be added *oblongirostris*, they are only varieties depending upon age, sex, habitat, or some other circumstance. The variable character on which they were founded must not obscure the fact that they have in common other characters, which are themselves permanent or semi-permanent. Such, in particular, is the number of vertebræ. " I have set myself," said Blanchard, " the task of determining it amongst a quantity of eels from every locality, in choosing those most dissimilar in the shape of the head, and I have always counted from 113 to 115 without any correlation between number of vertebræ and shape of head."

There are, then, both variable and permanent characters, and this distinction allows us to go forward without becoming lost in the natural history of the eel. The variations due to age, to sex, and to environmental conditions define, at most, phases in the life-history or local races. Three authors especially have studied them.

There was Jacoby, in 1889, with his study of the fisheries of Lake Comacchio, whose opinion in regard to flat and long beaked eels may be summarised in this way. The broad-nosed eels are sterile females, non-migratory, always greenish-yellow and spending their entire lives feeding. The sharp-nosed are on the contrary males or fertile females, which turn yellow during the early period of their growth and become silvery at the time of migration.

But is it credible that eels— we speak of the broad-nosed variety—which are fully equipped for reproduction (with well developed ovaries, and eggs perfectly visible although unprovided with a yolk) remain in some way " barren " instead of leaving, as the others do, the rivers and lakes to reach the nuptial rendezvous? Jacoby's hypothesis was unsatisfactory and called for further research, not more extensive, but conducted with a more critical mind. In fact, Petersen (1896) arrived at quite a different understanding. From the comparison of hundreds of eels from many places, he came to the following conclusions : (a)—The broad and the sharp-nosed eels arc only the extremes of a continuous series; (b)—The broad-nosed as well as the sharp-nosed may be male or female; (c)—The former can become silvery and reproduce as well as the latter; (d)—The former's snout becomes narrower and deeper in the course of sexual maturation.

On the whole we are dealing with small differences between individuals during their period of growth, and due in all probability to the environment.

In the course of his eel investigations, Schmidt (1914-1915) discovered and studied other characters, having the advantage over those previously used, of being measurable. The first was the maximum height of the body expressed as a percentage of the total length. The second was the ano-dorsal measurement expressed also as a percentage of the total length. It is expressed by the formula $(a - d) / l \times 100$, in which a, the pre-anal distance, is the length measured from the tip of the snout to the anus, d is the pre-dorsal distance measured from the tip of the

Table I. Evolution of Ideas on the Classification of European Eels

	Risso 1826	Cuvier 1829	Ekström 1835	Yarrell 1836	Kaup 1856	Blanchard 1866	Günther 1870	Moreau 1881	Modern Authors
	latirostris	Plat-bec	*latirostris* platyrhina	Grig-eel	platycephala ?capitone ?melanochir ?ancidda latirostris	latirostris	latirostris	platycephala latirostris	*Anguilla anguilla*
	mediorostris Verniau	Pimperneau		Glut-eel mediorostris	mediorostris	mediorostris	*vulgaris*	vulgaris	
	acutirostris	Long-bec	oxyrhina	acutirostris	?morena acutirostris	oblongirostris acutirostris			
					kieneri cuvieri bibroni savignyi ?marginata ?microptera ?altirostris		kieneri	kieneri	

snout to the first dorsal fin-ray, and l is the total length of the body from one end to the other (Fig. 52).

In the European eel, the ano-dorsal measurement varies from 10 to 13 per cent. of the length. It depends on the age and the habitat, but withal, this one trenchant character distinguishes the European eel at a glance from certain foreign species.

PERMANENT CHARACTERS AND THEIR STATISTICAL ANALYSIS

Let us now consider characters which depend neither upon age nor upon sex; those which, because they remain unchanged during the life-time of an individual, are known as *permanent characters*. But "permanent" in our present sense does not mean "constant"; these characters vary, in fact, between individuals of the same species from different populations, from within the same local group, even from the same brood. Returning to the example given by Blanchard, though the commonest number of vertebræ in a population be 115 there may exist, nevertheless, individuals with 114 vertebræ and others with 116, with 113 and with 117. The character fluctuates about a mean value in much the same way as a pendulum swings to either side of its position of equilibrium. In biology such behaviour of a character is known as *variation* or *fluctuation* and the study of fluctuation susceptible to measurement or counting is called *biometry*.

Schmidt used three permanent but variable characters in classifying eels: the number of vertebræ, the number of branchiostegal rays supporting the gill-membranes and the number of rays in the pectoral fins. Their study requires the use of a special technique, the *statistical method,* the basic principles of which will now be demonstrated.

As an example let us consider the sample of 127 eels from Copenhagen studied by Schmidt (1914). (Table II, p. 27). Among these were three eels with 111 vertebræ, five with 112 vertebræ, and so on to the two eels with 118 vertebræ which completed the series. The number most commonly occurring is 115. Thereafter, in order of frequency, we have 114 and 116, 113 and 117, and so on. We are, in fact, dealing with a variation whose frequencies in the sample being studied (and ultimately in the population from which that sample was drawn) may be said to have a *normal distribution* about a central value.

The numbers of vertebræ (x) and their observed frequencies (f) are set forth in columns I and II of Table II. We are now commencing to replace the various quantities under consideration by letter symbols, partly because this provides us with a shorthand to facilitate further discussion, partly because it leads us step by step towards certain statistical formulæ of general application, patterns of " labelled boxes " into which other similar data may be sorted and analysed.

The *sum of the observed frequencies* (Σf) is, of course, equal to the total number of individuals studied (n): $3 + 5 + 17 + \ldots = 127$. [In mathematics the Greek letter Σ (capital Sigma) is used to denote " The sum of all the values of — ", hence the sum of the observed frequencies is shortly written (Σf).]

The number of vertebræ (115) occurring most frequently in the sample is known as the *mode* (μ = Greek letter Mu), but the average number or *mean* ($\bar{x}$ = x bar) is the arithmetic mean of all the numbers of vertebræ observed. This is obtained by adding the partial products: (111×3) + (112×5) + (113×17) + ... and dividing the sum by 127. The answer to three places, is 114·677; this number of vertebræ has obviously no real existence, but is the value about which the particular character varies. The relation is expressed by the formula:—

$$\bar{x} = (\Sigma\ xf)/n.$$

We now construct a " frequency polygon " (Fig. 4) joining the points obtained when the numbers of vertebræ (x) are plotted along a horizontal axis and the corresponding frequencies observed (f) along a perpendicular. In this diagram the mode, or most frequent value, is the abcissa corresponding to the greatest vertical height; while the mean corresponds to the abcissa of the centre of gravity G of the polygon. The polygon thus presents a graphic image of the variability of the numbers of vertebræ in the sample of eels and *approximates* to that of the population from which it was drawn. Narrow at the base and

I JOHANNES SCHMIDT (1877—1933)

Danish oceanographer and biologist; discoverer of the
breeding-place of the European eel.

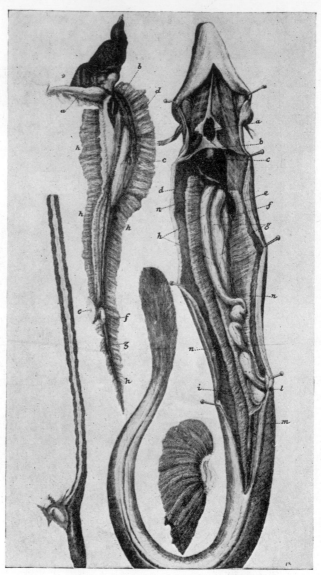

II DISSECTION OF A FEMALE EEL

Right: general view. *Left upper:* separate viscera. *Left lower:* kidneys and urinary bladder. Key: *a* heart (or oesophagus in left figure); *b* pericardium (or pancreas); *c* liver (or stomach); *d* gall bladder (or ovary); *e* pancreas; *f* swim-bladder (or urinary bladder); *g* stomach (or ovary); *h* intestine (or ovary); *i* urinary bladder; *l* anus; *m* kidney; *n* ovary (*after Mondini*)

very high it indicates a weak degree of variation; broad at the base and very low it would indicate a strong degree of variation. We notice also that it is nearly symmetrical. It would be still more so with a larger sample of eels from the same locality and would tend finally to a smooth bell-shaped curve, *the normal curve of distribution.*

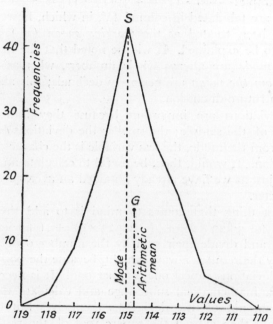

FIG. 4.   Polygon of variation for the number of vertebrac in 127 cels at Copenhagen.

G, centre of gravity of the polygon: its abcissa is the *mean value* of this characteristic; S, peak of the polygon: its abcissa is the *mode*, or most frequent value.

Returning now to the data tabulated in the first two columns of Table II, since the mean number of vertebræ in the sample is 114·677 we can consider the observed numbers 111, 112, etc. as more or less deviating from this average and express these deviations thus:—118 - 114·677 = + 3·323; 111 - 114·677 = - 3.677, and so on.

c

The deviation of a value from the average is therefore the algebraic difference between this value and the mean, written $(x - \bar{x})$. The algebraic numbers so obtained are known as *deviations from the mean* and are tabulated in column 3. In the same way we can define the *deviation from the mode* $(x - \mu)$, and calculate the deviations from the mode in the present example:—$118 - 115 = +3$; $117 - 115 = +2$, etc. These deviations are tabulated in column IV, in which, however, the mode has been treated as the *working mean* (x_m), a term presently to be explained. It will be noted that the *deviations from the mode* are always whole numbers, whereas the *deviations from the mean* are generally decimals; this also has a bearing on future discussion.

The deviations are important because they indicate the variability of the sample; the smaller the deviations from the mean or from the mode, the less variable is the character under consideration. It would, then, be useful to calculate an average deviation just as we have already obtained an average value of the character.

The first thing that comes to mind is to add the partial products: $(+3 \cdot 323 \times 2) + (+2 \cdot 323 \times 9) + (+1 \cdot 323 \times 22)$ $+ . . . . .$ and divide their sum by the number of eels. Unfortunately the result is always nought, because the positive and negative deviations cancel one another out! It is necessary to resort to a mathematical subterfuge and calculate the arithmetic mean, not of the deviations themselves but of their squares, and then extract the square root of the result. The quantity obtained is called the *standard deviation,* represented by the Greek letter σ (small Sigma) and given by the formula :—

$$\sigma = \pm \sqrt{\frac{\Sigma \ (x - \bar{x})^2}{n}}$$

There remains the difficulty that the calculations are troublesome on account of the decimals to be squared. This is disposed of by a further mathematical subterfuge. Instead of the true mean $(\bar{x})$, which is a decimal and the cause of all the trouble, we select as a *working mean* (x_m) a whole number close to the true mean. In the present case the mode $(\mu = 115)$ will serve us

TABLE II. RESULTS OF A STATISTICAL ANALYSIS OF THE CHARACTER. " NUMBER OF VERTEBRAE " IN A SAMPLE OF 127 EELS FROM COPENHAGEN.

I Number of Vertebræ (x)	II Frequency observed (f)	III Deviation from the Mean $(x-\bar{x})$	IV Deviation from the Working Mean $(x-x_m)$
118	2	+3·323	+3
117	9	+2·323	+2
116	22	+1·323	+1
115	43	+0·323	0
114	26	−0·677	−1
113	17	−1·677	−2
112	5	−2·677	−3
111	3	−3·677	−4

Number of individuals: $n = \sum f = 127$

Mean: $\bar{x} = \sum xf/n = 114\cdot677$

Working mean: $x_m = 115$ ($=$ Mode μ)

Standard deviation: $\sigma = \pm \sqrt{\dfrac{\sum(x-\bar{x})^2}{n}}$

or $\pm \sqrt{\dfrac{\sum(x-x_m)^2}{n} - \left(\dfrac{\sum(x-x_m)}{n}\right)^2}$

$= \pm 1\cdot402$

Probable error of the mean: $PE_{\bar{x}} = \pm 0\cdot6745 \dfrac{\sigma}{\sqrt{n}} = \pm 0\cdot0839$

The limits of the population mean: $\overline{X}$ (as opposed to the sample mean $\bar{x}$) may be assumed to be $\bar{x} \pm 5 \cdot PE_{\bar{x}} = 114\cdot677 \pm 0\cdot419$. Hence it is predicted that the population mean lies within the range 114·258–115·096.

very well, although we are not obliged to choose it; 114 or 116 would be equally satisfactory. As shown in column 4, since all the *deviations from the working mean* $(x - x_m)$ are integers the process of squaring is now rendered very easy. We return to the *standard deviation* σ by a transformation formula:—

$$\sigma = \pm \sqrt{\frac{\sum(x-x_m)^2}{n} - \left(\frac{\sum(x-x_m)}{n}\right)^2}$$

The derivation of this form is complicated and will not be attempted here; the interested reader will find it in Bertin

(1925) or in any good textbook of statistics, a selection of which is included in the bibliography at the end of the present chapter.

The standard deviation thus defined requires the calculation of the *sum of the squares of the deviations from the working* mean $\Sigma(x - x_m)^2$ and the *square of the sum of the deviations from the working mean* $[\Sigma(x - x_m)]^2$. These are given by :—

$$\Sigma(x - x_m)^2 = (2 \times 3^2) + (9 \times 2^2) + \ldots\ldots + (3 \times (-4)^2) = 263$$

and

$$[\Sigma(x - x_m)]^2 = ((2 \times 3) + (9 \times 2) + \ldots\ldots + (3 \times -4))^2 = 1681$$

Completing the calculation as indicated by the formula, we discover that in the example chosen, namely the sample of 127 eels from Copenhagen, the index of variability* or *standard deviation of the mean* $\sigma = \pm 1 \cdot 402$.

So far we have only translated into mathematical terms the variations observed in the numbers of vertebræ in our relatively small sample of eels. We now want to know what would happen to the mean as the number of eels studied became larger and larger, tending towards infinity. We want, in fact, to know what our sample can tell us about the population from which it was drawn, which is the whole *raison d'être* of biological sampling and statistical analysis.

Only the calculation of probabilities can answer this new question. The deviations which we have noted can be compared, in fact, to errors of measurement. They are, as it were, Nature's margins of error in realising a certain average type and, together with the possible errors due to our sampling, they may be assessed by the "Law of Error" known as Gauss' Law.

We now meet with a new index, the *probable error of the mean* :—

$$PE_{\bar{x}} = \pm 0 \cdot 6745 \frac{\sigma}{\sqrt{n}}$$

(The term $\frac{\sigma}{\sqrt{n}}$ is the *standard error of the mean*).

---

* Another index of variability is the *standard deviation of the mode*, given by $S = \pm \sqrt{\frac{\Sigma(x - \mu)^2}{n}}$. But S is greater than σ and it can be shown that this must always be so. The sum of squares of deviations beginning

The present significance of this index is as follows. If, instead of studying only 127 eels, we had considered a far greater number, with 115 still the mode or commonest number of vertebræ, the mean or average number of vertebræ would almost certainly lie within the limits $x - 5.\text{PE}_{\bar{x}}$ and $x + 5.\text{PE}_{\underline{x}}$, i.e., in the present case between 114·258 and 115·096. We can thus predict that in the population from which the sample is drawn the commonest number of vertebræ or *population mode* (M) will be 115, and that the *population mean* $(\bar{X})$ will lie within the range 114·258 – 115·096. Schmidt applied a similar technique to the analysis of samples from many other regions, and tabulated the predicted population modes and means as we have done here and in Tables III and IV, pp. 30 and 31.

In the two memoirs already mentioned, entitled "Eel Investigations", as well as in a third memoir on the classification of freshwater eels, Schmidt (1914-1915) studied nearly 2,000 eels from all over Europe, and about 1,000 from Japan and the U.S.A. This important material enabled him to establish that all European eels have sensibly the same average number of vertebræ. Practically all have 114, 115 or 116 vertebræ. The mode of all the polygons of variation is 115. The polygons themselves are nearly superposable (Fig. 5). Here then are the figures obtained from stations as far as possible from each other.

Similar results were obtained from the study of the branchiostegal rays and of the pectoral rays. It may be concluded from this that there is only one species of eel in Europe and North Africa, the species known as *Anguilla anguilla* (or *Anguilla vulgaris*). Throughout its vast range, which extends from the North Cape to the Azores and Egypt, this species is perfectly

---

from the mean is always smaller than the sum of the squares of deviations beginning from any other value. Thus σ is always chosen as the better criterion of variability.

The reader who seeks further information concerning the *probable error of the mean* in any modern textbook of statistics is likely to be disappointed, or to find, at best, a briefly derogatory note. Statistics, like other sciences, has made advances since 1914 when Schmidt employed this index in analysing his data. We retain his method here solely because he used it and because these are his results and as such part of the history of ichthyology; not because we are unaware of the newer methods of testing the significance of means and of the differences between means.

TABLE III

Locality	Mode μ	Mean $\bar{x}$	Predicted limits of the Population Mean, $\overline{X}$
Iceland	115	114·726	114·405—115·046
Denmark	115	114·680	114·415—114·945
Ireland	115	114·726	114·308—115·144
Bayonne	115	114·671	114·378—114·964
Sete	115	114·888	114·540—115·236
Comacchio	115	114·603	114·226—114·980
Azores	115	114·772	114·465—115·679

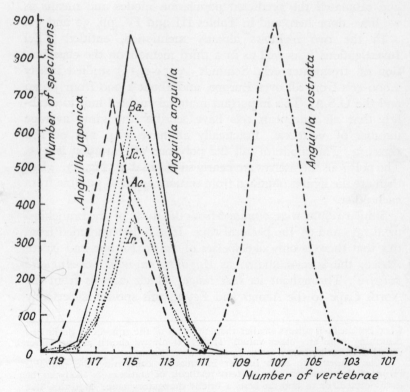

FIG. 5. Polygons of variation for the numbers of vertebrae in *Anguilla anguilla*, *Anguilla japonica* and *Anguilla rostrata*.

For the European eel, separate polygons are shown (dotted) for populations of the Azores (*Ac*), Bayonne (*Ba*), Ireland (*Ir*) and Iceland (*Ic*).

homogeneous. No distinct races or local varieties can be discovered among the individuals composing it.

Now let us examine the eels from Japan and the United States. Those from Japan constitute a species known as *Anguilla japonica,* which is closely related to the European eel, by the number of its vertebræ. The American eel, *Anguilla rostrata* is, on the contrary, distinctly different from the two others in its vertebral average which is around 107. This must be borne in mind when distinguishing between the larvæ of these different species.

EELS AND BLENNIES

Schmidt was not merely content with a biometrical study, far-reaching though it was, of the genus *Anguilla.* He wanted to compare the European eel, essentially a migratory species, with another species of fish essentially sedentary. His choice fell naturally on *Zoarces viviparus,* a kind of blenny well-known around the coasts of the North Sea and the Baltic. As the specific name indicates *Zoarces* is viviparous, and the young do not move far from the parents. Finally, the comparison is made the easier in that the average number of vertebræ is nearly the same in *Anguilla anguilla* and *Zoarces viviparus.*

In one of his memoirs, published in 1917, Schmidt gives all the values, frequencies, averages, etc. for the number of vertebræ in about 15,000 *Zoarces* obtained from 61 localities in Northern Europe. Now, far from finding a homogeneity comparable with that of the eel, he found a multitude of local races. As an example we may take the deep Mariager Fjord on the east coast of Jutland which stretches for 50 kilometres (Fig. 6). Five stations taken along this fjord, and consequently 10 to 20 km. distant from one another have given the results tabulated in Table IV.

Thus, the *Zoarces* living in the same fjord, one at the entrance (station 15) and the other at the head (station 19), differ more markedly in the number of their vertebræ, than the eels originating from places as far apart as Iceland and the Azores. A more remarkable contrast at first sight could hardly be found. Yet it is explained by the biology of the fishes.

TABLE IV

Locality	Mode μ	Mean x̄	Predicted Limits of the Population Mean, X̄
Station 14	117	117·37	116·89—117·85
,, 15	115	115·43	114·78—116·08
,, 16	110	110·99	110·15—111·83
,, 17	110	110·18	109·75—110·61
,, 19	109	109· 30	108·90—109·70

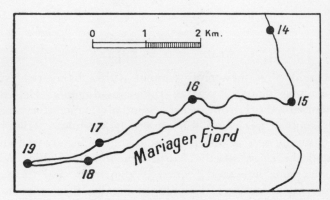

FIG. 6. Schmidt's stations for the study of *Zoarces viviparus* in the Mariager Fjord (Denmark).

On the one hand, *Zoarces* is sedentary and is subjected, from one generation to another, to the same external influences of temperature, salinity, food, etc. These factors induce differences even between neighbouring populations, which become accentuated in course of time. On the other hand, eels are migratory and, what is more to the point, all the European eels have the one spawning ground. The local action of the environment cannot then make itself felt in these animals since all of them spend their critical early larval life in the Sargasso Sea, where also there is almost certainly cross-breeding between individuals coming from every country of Europe.

The contrast between sedentary and migratory species is here brought to its maximum. It is not, however, peculiar to eels or to *Zoarces*. Bertin (1925) has shown the existence of innumerable local forms in the stickleback, which is, however, a little less sedentary than *Zoarces viviparus*. The sardines and herrings, although migratory, are divided into local races, distinguished by the proportions of their bodies, the number of their vertebræ, etc. The biologist sees in this the proof that their migrations are restricted and consist, for each population, in seasonal movements only, from the deep sea towards the coast and *vice versa*. The reverse is seen in the salmon, shad, lamprey and mullet, which do not seem to vary throughout large areas.

BIBLIOGRAPHY

BERTIN, L. Recherchcs bionomicales, biométricales et systématiques sur les épinoches. *Ann. Inst. Océan.* N.S., Vol. II, (Paris, 1925).

BLANCHARD, E. *Les poissons des eaux douces de la France.* (Paris, 1866).

CONNOLLY, T. G. and SLUCKIN, W. *Introduction to Statistics for the Social Sciences.* (London, Cleaver-Hume, 2nd edn., 1957).

CUVIER, G. *Le règne animal distribué d'apres son organisation,* 2nd edn., Vol. II. (Paris, 1829).

FISHER, R. A. *Statistical Methods for Research Workers.* (Edinburgh, Oliver & Boyd, 1936).

JACOBY, L. *Der Fischfang in der Lagune von Comacchio.* (Berlin, 1880).

KAUP, J. J. *Catalogue of Apodal Fish.* (London, 1856).

MATHER, K. *Statistical Analysis in Biology.* (London, Methuen, 1946).

MORONEY, N. J. *Facts and Figures.* (London, Penguin, 1951).

PETERSEN, C. G. J. The common eel gets a particular breeding-dress before its emigration to the sea. *Rep. Dan. Biol. St.,* Vol. V, (Copenhagen, 1896).

RISSO, A. *Histoire naturelle de l'Europe méridionale.* Vol. III, (Paris, 1826).

SCHMIDT, J. First report on eel investigations. *Rapp. Pr. Verb. Cons. Int. Expl. Mer.,* Vol. XVIII, (Copenhagen, 1914). Second report on eel investigations. *Idem,* Vol. XXIII, (1916). On the classification of the freshwater eels, *Med. Komm. Hav. Fisk.,* Vol. IV, (Copenhagen, 1914). Zoarces viviparus and local races of the same. *C.R. Trav. Lab. Carlsberg,* Vol. XIII, (Copenhagen, 1917).

SIMPSON, G. G. & ROE, A. *Quantitative Zoology,* (New York, McGraw Hill, 1939).

YARRELL, W. *A History of British Fishes,* Vol. II, (London, 1836).

YULE, G. U. and KENDALL, M. G. *Theory of Statistics.* (London, Griffin, 1937).

CHAPTER III

Growth of the Yellow Eel

IN feeding and growth, the eel passes during its life-time through five phases of markedly unequal length.

(1) An *embryonic phase* of a few days during which the animal is nourished exclusively by the food reserves in the yolk of the egg.

(2) A *larval phase* of two or three years in the course of which the animal feeds on microscopic organisms in the plankton.

(3) An *inactive period* of a few months coinciding with the metamorphosis of the leptocephalus into the elver.

(4) A *growth phase* of some years, during which the yellow eel becomes omnivorous and frequents the rivers and lakes.

(5) A final *phase of inactivity* of about a year, coinciding with sexual maturity and with the transformation of the yellow eel into the silver eel.

This chapter is devoted to the study of the yellow eel's growth phase, between the end of the first period of inactivity and the beginning of the second. Its limits are then perfectly defined. After an account of the methods of study, we shall show how the growth of the eel depends in the first place on its sex and its food; and secondly on the temperature and the living space available to it.

REARING AND MEASUREMENT

The best methods for studying the growth of eels are the direct, by actually rearing them, and the indirect, by measuring them and observing the seasonal growth of their various parts.

Rearing eels offers extreme difficulties which are almost insurmountable. Reliable statistical results can only be obtained from a large number of individuals and this involves three main losses: through death from natural causes, through escapes and through cannibalism, a particularly striking example of which will be given later. Measurements can be made on the size (total length) or on the weight, but these cannot be taken as reliable criteria of age, particularly in poikilothermic (cold-blooded) animals, since they are influenced to an exaggerated degree by their environment.

Heredity also exerts a strong influence. It is necessary therefore, to obtain results of a general nature, to use biometrical methods, which means measuring hundreds or thousands of individuals from a given locality in order to construct a polygon of variation of their size.

In studying fishes thus, there become evident three main types:

(1) The clear-cut case (Fig. 7, A), in fishes like the stickleback, which have both a short reproductive period, and a short life. The individuals born, for instance, in April 1942 form a group clearly distinct from individuals born in April 1941, and so on.

(2) The average case (B), as in most Clupeoids (herrings, sardines) and Gadoids (cod, whiting), which have a short reproductive period, but a long life. The youngest annual groups are clearly-marked; the others encroach more and more on each other.

(3) The ill-defined (C), are those which, like the eel, have a long reproductive period and a long life. All the annual groups overlap, and it becomes impossible, merely on size alone, to tell the age of the individuals.

This was indicated by the polygon of variations actually obtained by Gandolfi Hornyold (1930) based on measurements made of 596 yellow eels from the lake of Tunis. This polygon (Fig. 12) has a number of peaks, and it would be quite wrong, as we shall see, to regard them as indications of annual groups. The overlapping of these groups also makes it impossible to draw any conclusions as to the age of an individual taken at random.

Therefore, measurement of length or weight, like the method

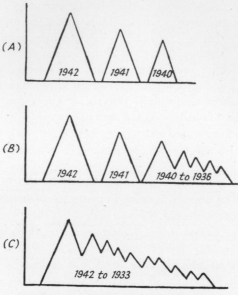

Fig. 7. Diagrammatic represen-
tations of annual groups in a
species: (*A*) with brief reproduc-
tion-period and short life; (*B*)
with the same but long life; (*C*)
with both long. The eel belongs
to the last category.

of rearing, cannot be used to determine the age and growth of
an eel. There remain only those methods which are based on
the observation of seasonal growth of separate organs. Let us,
therefore, examine in turn the results obtained from readings
of the scales and the otoliths.

SCALE READINGS

It is not generally known that eels have scales. If, however,
one examines carefully their smooth slimy skin, one sees a multitude of small oblong patches placed at right angles to each
other and forming a kind of mosaic (Fig. 8). These
are rudimentary scales embedded in the skin and not over-

FIG. 8. Arrangement of scales in the skin of an eel.

lapping as do those of most other fishes. Their length varies from 7 to 8 mm. in the largest individuals. A good way to study them consists of rubbing the eel with a cloth and talcum powder, then, after it has been cleared of the mucus, scraping the fish with a scalpel. The scrapings are put into a tube containing a little water, which is then shaken, and the water renewed again and again. The scales become separated from each other and become sufficiently clean after a few days to be examined under the microscope.

Each scale, as Baudelot (1873) showed, is composed of an oval, transparent plaque on which are disposed, to the number of about a thousand, and in almost regularly concentric zones, some very little plaquettes which appear light or dark according to the method of lighting them. The plaquettes are in relief and are soluble in acid. It can be demonstrated that they are formed of the variety of calcium carbonate to which mineralogists have given the name ' aragonite '. Conversely, it is possible to dissolve their support without dissolving the scales themselves by treatment with soda or potash.

What is the significance of the concentric zones on the scales? Baudelot said that they are *perhaps* zones of growth. Thomson, himself the author of a beautiful work on the periodic growth of scales, wrote in 1904, that " those of the eel show concentric rings, without our being able to say whether they are annual or not." Gemzoé (1906) is more definite. The observation on which he relies is that the eels, in the course of their life in fresh water, pass through alternate periods of summer activity and winter rest—in other words, periods of growth and cessation of growth—which must be translated into the structure of their scales as it is in those of other fishes. According to him, the broad zones, covered with plaquettes, are the zones of summer growth which separate the narrow bands corresponding to successive winters. *Every year, the eel enlarges its scales by one*

summer zone and one winter zone, somewhat as a tree trunk
is enlarged. It is sufficient to count the broad or the narrow
zones to know how many years it has been alive (Fig. 9). Such
a method of determining the age by the scales is general for all
fishes. In the eel, we meet, unfortunately, a certain number of
difficulties, which restricts its use.

(1) *The scales appear late.*—The first are developed in the
yellow eel when it is 15 or 20 cms. long and already, as shown
by other methods, in its 5th, 6th or
7th year. In taking an average age
6 years, we risk making an error
of one year more or less, which
cannot be seen in the scales alone.

(2) *The scales appear in succession.*—The first appear towards
the middle of the flanks; the last
in the front part of the trunk and
on the tail. They do not, therefore, indicate the same age. The
oldest must still be looked for in
the region of the lateral line, a
little in front of the anus. Gandolfi Hornyold (1937) had the
patience to examine 1,400 scales,
from nine different parts of an eel
of large dimensions. He found
only one, that is 0·07 per cent of
the total number, which had the
maximum number of zones. It
is clear that less persevering

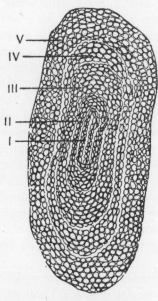

FIG. 9. Eel scale with five
zones of annual growth
(*after G. Gemzoe*).

work might not have permitted the discovery of this exceptional
scale.

(3) *The growth of the scales is irregular.*—It is not unusual
to find zones of incomplete growth, and doubtless others may
be missing. Finally, after a certain age, the scales cease to grow.
The difference between the number of zones on a scale, and
that on an otolith, increases from this point onwards.

To sum up, the scales of the eel must be regarded as rudimentary and of no interest as a measure of the passage of time.

OTOLITH READINGS

The place of the scale as a precise determination of age must be taken by the otolith, as the works of Ehrenbaum and Marukawa (1914), and Gandolfi Hornyold (beginning in 1920), have shown. The otoliths (σῦς, ὠτός, ear; λίθος stone) are concretions of calcium carbonate lodged in the ears of fishes. There are three on each side: the lapillus, the astericus, and the sagitta. This last, the largest, is the only one that can be used to determine the age. It reaches a length of 7 mm. in the largest eels and appears to the naked eye as a whitish body, concave on one face and convex on the other, with a slight groove on the convex face (Fig. 10).

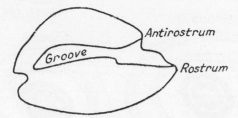

FIG. 10.   Convex face of an eel otolith.

The technique of preparing the otolith for microscopic examination is as follows: the cranium is opened longitudinally with a pair of scissors, the brain is removed and a search is made on each side with a magnifying glass for the sagitta which is extracted with forceps and cleaned between the thumb and forefinger. Using the method evolved by Tåning (1938), it is embedded in a small block of plaster mixed with manganese oxide black, and the block being hardened, grinding on a carborundum stone produces a transverse or longitudinal section which shows up white against the black mass of the block. This, in a Petri dish containing xylol, creosote, or turpentine to clear it, is examined under the binocular microscope; thin sections can thus be made which can be photographed by transmitted light.

In the middle of an otolith prepared in this way can be seen a kind of nucleus comprising two tightly packed zones (Plate III). These are the sea rings (*Meeresringe* of the German authors) representing that part of the otolith laid down in the leptocephalus stage and during the life of the elver until it reaches the coast. The alternating broad and narrow zones

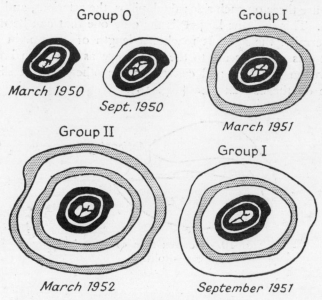

Fig. 11. Determination of an eel's age from its otoliths.

The black centre zones correspond to the marine life as a leptocephalus, the large light and the narrow shaded zones to summers and winters respectively in fresh water.

which surround it represent, on the other hand, the successive stages of the life of the eel in the fresh waters. As Gandolfi Hornyold says: "The broad clear zones of the otolith correspond to the broad, sprinkled calcareous plaquettes of the scales; the narrow dark zones of the otolith correspond to the narrow zones in the scales, without plaquettes." But while the scales 'mark' irregularly and then only after the 6th year, the otolith registers season by season, all stages of the animal's life. Hence its greater reliability for determining the age of the eel.

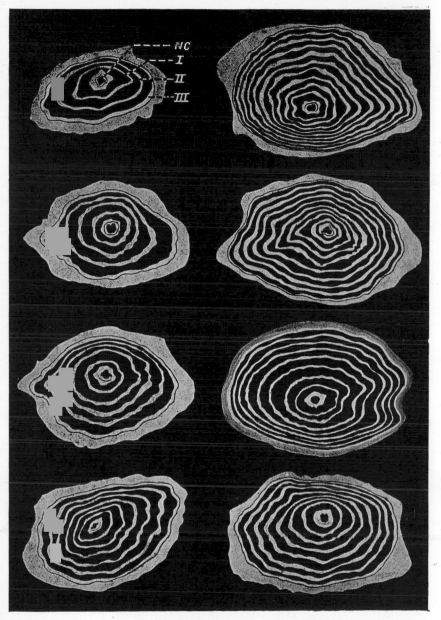

III   OTOLITHS OF AN EEL
AFTER THREE TO TEN YEARS IN FRESH WATER

Seen by dark-ground illumination, so that the black rings correspond
to the translucent summer zones, the white rings to the denser winter
ones. *NC:* nucleus formed in the sea; I—III, first winter zones in
fresh water.

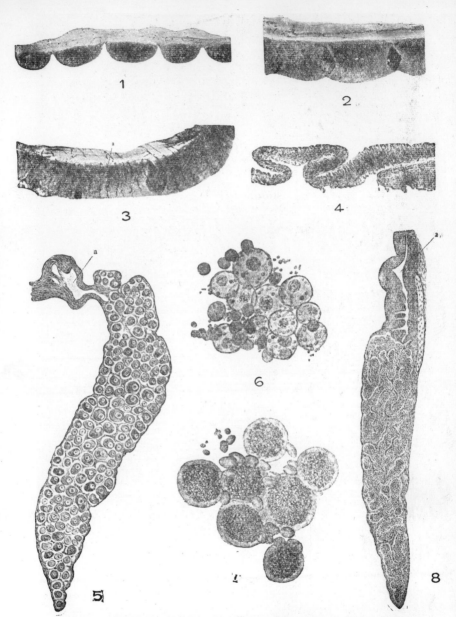

IV GENITAL ORGANS OF THE EEL—DETAILS

1—4. Transformation of the lobulate organ into a frilled organ in eels of 30—40 cm. 5. Transverse section of the ovary in a 46 cm. silver eel; the vas deferens (*a*) is degenerate. 8. Transverse section of the testis in a 39 cm. silver eel: the vas deferens (*a*) is quite continuous (*after F. Mazza*). 6. Oocytes and adipose cells. 7. Ova filled with yolk granules (*after Gandolfi Hornyold*)

Let us take the otolith, reduced to its central portion (Fig. 11), of an elver that reaches the European coast in March 1955. Spawned in the Sargasso Sea in March 1952, it is exactly three years old. A year later, in March 1953, there is added to the nucleus of the otolith the first summer zone (broad and clear) and the first winter zone (dark and narrow). If we represent the first winter zone by the figure 1, all we need do is add 1 + 3 to obtain the total age of the fish. By September 1956, the narrow zone is surrounded by a new zone formed during the course of the summer. The eel is now more than four years old but not quite five : it is in its fifth year. By March 1957 the second winter ring has appeared and the total age is now 2 + 3 = 5 years.

Thus, alternatively, the number N of the winter zones signifies that the eel has lived N + 3 years or that it will have reached that number at some time in the following year.

Following the practice of Gandolfi Hornyold, we can speak of eels of group O, group I, group II, etc., which have respectively O. I, II, etc., narrow zones in their otoliths. The explanation already given demonstrates what is meant by these terms.

In the North Sea, and especially in the Baltic, the arrival of the elvers at the coast takes place during May to June only, instead of from January to March. That is why German ichthyologists follow Ehrenbaum and Marukawa in considering the year completed only if there is added to the winter zone a beginning of a summer zone. The year-group is thus indicated, according to them, not by the number of the narrow zones, but by the number of broad zones, less one. As a result there is a slight adjustment to be made in comparing the work of different authors.

IRREGULARITIES IN GROWTH

To talk of ' laws of growth ' in eels is to use a pretentious term. It is more a question of empirical laws which lack the support of precise experiment. As has already been pointed out, such experiments are almost impossible to carry out, so we have to be content with correlating the size of the individual with the number of zones in its otoliths. An average length

D

and weight can, however, be ascertained for each year-group for each locality.

Before arriving at our conclusions let us review briefly the works in which, over a third of a century, the indispensable data for this kind of research have been accumulated. The first was in 1908, in a work in which Gemzoe studied the growth of the Danish eels using only the scales. He affirms, wrongly, that they always appear during the third year of life in fresh water. This error was repeated in 1909 by Schneider who, in his memoir on the growth of Swedish eels, used in place of the scales, the zones on the vertebræ as a means of measuring age.

Ehrenbaum and Marukawa (1914) were the first to use the otoliths. They carried out their researches on many hundreds of eels from the lower courses of the Elbe and other rivers of Northern Germany. Their disciples Haempel and Neresheimer (1914) extended these investigations to the eels of Comacchio (Italy) and of Lake Vrana (Dalmatia). Wundsch (1916) studied the eels of the numerous lakes and pools of Prussia and Silesia. In a posthumous memoir, Marcus (1919) made a critical survey of all the previous works and gave the results in his direct observation of more than 9,000 eels.

Between these times, Gandolfi Hornyold, an accomplished naturalist of a cosmopolitan type, visited Spain, France, Switzerland, Italy and Tunisia, searching for material for study. His numerous notes give the measurements and the ages of nearly 10,000 yellow or silver eels. They constitute an inexhaustible source of information which their author, unfortunately, did not always know how to interpret.

Let us quote in conclusion a work by Tesch (1928) on the sex and growth of eels in Dutch waters. The 4000 specimens studied by this author bring the total number of eels on which the following conclusions are based to about 25,000.

The most obvious thing about the growth of the yellow eels is its extreme irregularity. The dimensions, and above all the weight, of one individual may be five times as great as those of another individual of the same age. Two individuals of the same length may have very different weights according as the one is thicker than the other or its tissues are denser. Between eels from the same locality and, more especially, between populations from different localities, big differences can be observed in the development of the scales, and in the relations between size, weight, age, etc.

Let us go back, to state these ideas precisely, to the polygon of variation in size of the 596 eels from Tunis studied by Gandolfi Hornyold (1930). Instead of considering these eels as a whole, we can divide them, thanks to the otolith, into six year-groups, and study each of them separately. We will, however, confine ourselves to the groups VI, VII, and VIII which are the most abundantly represented (Fig. 12).

The first thing we see is that these groups largely overlap. The extremes of length are 31 and 46 cm. for group VI, 31 and 51 cm. for group VII, and 32 and 56 cm. for group VIII. The second is that there is always, among the eels of one year-group, a certain number of individuals which grow more quickly than the others. This advance-guard gives rise to a horizontal prolongation of the polygon of variation. The individuals composing it can be compared, perhaps, to cyclists who detach themselves from the main group in a race, and surpass their rivals to such an extent that the field is well spread out.

Finally, the last year-groups come together again, and an eel of 45 cm. could belong to any one of groups VI, VII, VIII, IX, and X. To judge an eel's age solely by its length, would be to risk an error of one to five years either way.

INFLUENCE OF SEX

Among the irregularities of growth, must be distinguished those which are truly irregular, due to individual idiosyncrasies, and those which are, on the contrary, only the manifestation of internal influences, such as sex, or of external influences, such as temperature, living space, and food. Even without experience, it is possible to recognise these " false " irregularities and to relate them to their respective causes.

The growth of the female surpasses that of the male in intensity and duration. In the same interval of time, females will put on a greater amount of flesh and at the same age are longer, thicker and heavier than the individuals of the other

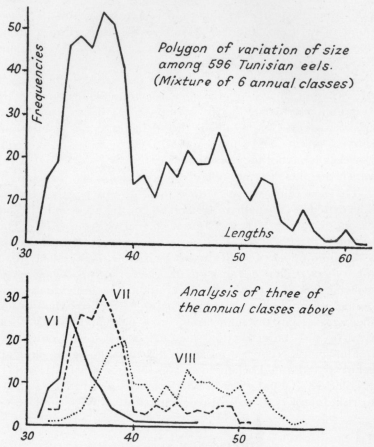

FIG. 12. Study of annual groups of eels in the lake
of Tunis (*after Gandolfi Hornyold*).

sex. They are also longer lived. All the old eels captured in
fresh water or kept in aquaria are females. Sometimes a half
a century old, they reach a length of 140 cm. and weigh
several kilogrammes. The males, on the contrary, rarely exceed
a length of 50 cm. and live at most 15 years.

Let us examine the growth curve from different localities
(Fig. 13). In all, we see the dotted lines corresponding to the
females detach themselves from those of males above a certain

age (year-groups II and IV) then rise more sharply and persist longer. The final difference is particularly marked in the eels of the Lake of Tunis and of the Albufera of Valencia in Spain.

The influence of sex on growth is a general fact of which one will find numerous examples in the syntheses of D'Ancona

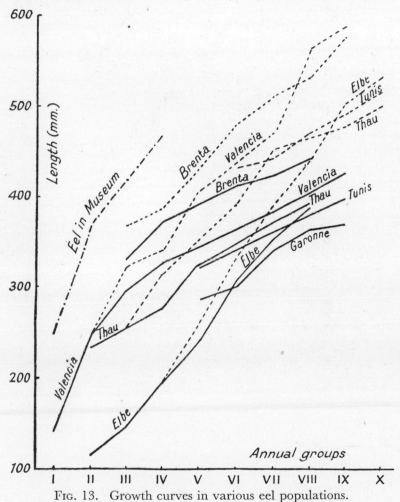

FIG. 13. Growth curves in various eel populations.

Continuous lines refer to non-differentiated and male individuals, broken ones to females, in which growth is always more rapid and prolonged.

(1937) and of Fage and Veillet (1938). In practically all the species, there is an antagonism between growth and development. The more rapid the development, that is to say the earlier sexual maturity is reached, the smaller the size of the individual. That is what usually happens to the males, whose precocious development inhibits the growth of the body.

Extraordinary cases of longevity are known, where the female eels have been prevented, for one reason or another, from making their reproductive migration. Gandolfi Hornyold has summarized them in a work published in 1935. The first example that he gives is one of a female 110 cm. long, and 2,500 gm. in weight, which died of cold during the rigorous winter of 1928, after having been kept for 24 years at the Institute of Pisciculture of the University of Toulouse. An albino eel kept in the aquarium at Trocadero (near Cadiz) from 1913 to 1946 reached a length of 80 cm. A case often cited is the eel brought up from 1828 to 1865 by the family of Professor Desmaret, of Alfort. Despite the smallness of its habitat —a simple earthenware pan—this eel had reached at the end of its days the record dimensions of 140 cm.

Gandolfi Hornyold calls attention finally to the attempted re-stocking of Lake Cauma. This is situated in the Engadine at an altitude of 3000 feet and possesses neither tributaries nor outlets. Elvers having been put into it in 1882, the eels fished 50 years later, in 1932, by the local hotel syndicate measured from 50 to 130 cm. For the most part they were very thin and gave every indication of degeneration. Few of them had traces of the nuptial dress with silvering and large eyes, and in all of them the ovaries were in a state of regression.

INFLUENCE OF TEMPERATURE

The influence of temperature and, as a consequence, of the habitat is, like the influence of sex, manifest in all fishes. D'Ancona (1937) remarked that Mediterranean fishes have a more rapid development and a more limited growth than those of the North Sea or the North Atlantic. They mature more

quickly and remain smaller. Temperature also affects the proportions of the body in accelerating the growth of one or
another part. It can also affect the number of vertebræ, fin-
rays, cutaneous plaques, and so on, and can determine the
formation of local breeds. Its action is often combined with
that of salinity. Bertin (1925) demonstrated this in the
stickleback.

In eels, the period of growth is of course divided into periods
of activity and periods of rest. Cold inhibits their reflexes; and
they are active for instance in France only for a variable period
which extends from March or April to October or November.
In Sweden and Norway, the period is more restricted. On the
other hand, it is more widespread in the southern climates.
During the winter, the eels remain immobile in the mud and
take but little nourishment. They show, as do many other
animals, a winter lethargy, and this seasonal rhythm is reflected
in their scales and otoliths.

After these generalisations, let us go back, as before, to the
growth curve (Fig. 13). Three assertions can be made:

(1) Growth is more rapid in the southern stations than in the
northern.

(2) The influence of the temperature is especially marked
in the early years. The curves which start by being far apart
finish by drawing together and crossing. Eels of group III have
an average of 14 cm. in the Elbe, 25 cm. in the Étang de Thau
(S. France), 29 cm. in the Albufera of Valencia and 33 cm. in
the Brenta, near Venice. Those of group VIII, in the same
places have averages of 39, 40 and 44 cm. The extremes of
size are reduced, therefore, from 18 to 5 cm. in the space of five
years.

(3) The general form of the curves is that of an S, and is
known as sigmoid, which expresses growth in terms of time in
the majority of animals. This would be clearer still if, instead
of considering only the linear growth, the growth in weight
could be included.

For the action of temperature on the phenomena of life,
biologists often invoke the rule of Van't Hoff or the coefficient
of temperature. For every 10 degrees rise in temperature, they
say, the speed of such phenomena is increased by a certain

coefficient, which is between 2 and 3 : " an egg develops some three times as quickly at 25°C than at 15°C, a plant grows about three times as as quickly at 25°C than at 15°C, an ant walks about three times as fast at 25°C than at 15°C ". (Bohn).   Actually, the temperature coefficient decreases proportionally to the increase in temperature.   The rule of Van't Hoff is, therefore, not exact, and must be replaced by the law of Arrhenius, or of the *coefficient of decreasing temperature*. While the first rule is expressed by a curve rising indefinitely (Fig. 14 *a*), the second is expressed in a sigmoid curve (*b*). As the temperature continues to rise, it can be seen that the intensity of the biological phenomena passes a maximum and finishes by cancelling itself out.   The representative curve possesses, therefore, besides its ascending part with its point of inflection, a descending part which follows it and meets the axis of the abscissa following in a somewhat pronounced angle.   (Fig. 14c.)   It was a curve of this kind that Matisse (1919) obtained in his studies of the effect of heat and cold on living activities, e.g. locomotion in the snail, respiration in plants, and so on.

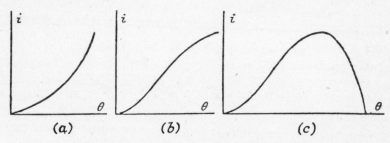

(a)   (b)   (c)

FIG. 14. Relation between temperature and speed of a reaction.

(*a*) van t'Hoff's rule;   (*b*) Law of Aarhenius;   (*c*) Law of Matisse.

Of course, in these researches it is not so much temperature that intervenes as the quantity of heat—which can be expressed in calories—taken in by the organism in the course of the experiment. In other words, the intensity i of the phenomenon is the function of two independent variables : temperature, θ and time t, or mathematically $i = f(\theta, t)$. It is only when t

is kept constant, that $i = f(\theta)$ as expressed by the curves of
Arrhenius and of Matisse.

Let us apply these facts to the growth of the eel. The graphs
in Fig. 13 represent it as a function of time and of the various
stations considered. To study the action of temperature, we
must choose two consecutive annual groups, for example, III
and IV, and determine the differences in the average length of
the eels in these two groups. We should then have the increase
in their lengths in the course of a year, or, in other words, their
rate of growth, which must be related to the quantity of heat
received at the different stations during the same lapse of time.

We are, unfortunately, very far from being able to do this.
The average temperature, and, more especially, the total of
the calories taken in, are by no means known with precision.
Such experiments should be made in the laboratory, not in the
field, and the eel, as we know, does not permit such investigations. It is the most deplorable subject one can imagine for the
study of growth.

INFLUENCE OF THE ENVIRONMENT

It is a curious general law that the size of an animal varies
directly with its living space. The growth of molluscs, planar-
ians, leeches, tadpoles, and the like, is in proportion to the
capacity of the aquaria in which they are reared. It seems to
be the same for the eel. Gandolfi Hornyold reported that
elvers kept in captivity in bottles became truly dwarf eels, in
spite of abundant food. He had eels sent from the pools of
Grande Brière, near Nantes, and reared them in a tank of one
cubic metre in the Jardin des Plantes in Paris. After three years,
these eels were markedly smaller than those of the same age
which had remained in their original place.

We shall see, later on, what such observations mean when
compared with that of Professor Desmaret's eel reared in
an earthenware pan which, as mentioned above, reached 140
cm. in 37 years.

Without varying the capacity, we can increase or diminish
the number of occupants, which amounts to altering the
amount of space available to each of them. By varying the

density of the population, the influence of the space is, therefore, reduced to a question of competition and, more particularly, competition for food.

It is in this light that Bellini (1907) made observations and experiments on eel culture in the lagoon of Comacchio, of 40,000 hectares, divided into a series of pools or *valli* (p. 106). Bellini first noted that the average weight of eels fished in each *valle* is in inverse proportion to the number of individuals per hectare. The more numerous the eels, the smaller they are.

TABLE V

Valli	Eels per Hectare	Average weight
Mezzano..........................	186	330 gr.
Bosco [N. of Isola].........	213	116 ,,
Ussarola [E. of Campo]...	261	100 ,,

Passing to the experimental stage, Bellini divided a *valle* into a series of compartments as nearly as possible identical in capacity (400 cubic metres), depth, salinity, temperature, vegetation, plankton, and so on. Each of the compartments received a pre-determined number of elvers with or without a certain number of mullet and atherines (silversides). Finally, the animals were either left to fend for themselves or were artificially fed with worms, slugs, powdered blood, or waste from the abattoirs, at regular intervals. The results at the end of four years are expressed in the following table

TABLE VI

No.	Eels	Mullets	Atherines	Complementary food	Average length of eels (cm.)	Average weight of eels (gr.)
1	158	42	1,260	—	55	190
2	79	42	1,260	—	56	195
3	158	42	1,260	Yes	57	255
4	158	0	0	Yes	58	260
5	79	0	0		66	345

Comparison of 1 and 2 shows the influence of the density of population on eels. Comparison of 1 and 3 shows the influence of an additional food. The competition from the mullets and atherines is shown by comparing 3 and 4. Hence in combining two by two the results obtained in the different compartments it is possible to demonstrate that the *quantity of food*, much more than capacity of the compartment, is the dominant factor in the growth of eels. Fidora (1951) obtained analogous results from his experiments.

INFLUENCE OF FOOD

The preceding observations foreshadow what will be clearly demonstrated by the following facts: *that the increase in the size and weight of eels is more a question of food than anything else.*

(1) We recall that the life of an eel follows a seasonal rhythm, and consists alternately of periods of summer feeding and a state of almost complete cessation of activity in winter. That the first predominates in the south and the second in the north, is explained in part by the single consideration of the difference of growth between southern and northern localities, in which the temperature acts through the medium of food requirements.

(2) Audige (1921) has compared the growth of trout, carp, and roach preserved under natural conditions and in water kept at constant temperature. Provided the latter is near the optimum (about 25°C for the Cyprinids, and 15°C for the Salmonids), its effect is clearly to accelerate both feeding and growth. Specimens not subject to seasonal rhythm become 3 or 4 times bigger than the controls. It is reasonable to suppose that analogous experiments carried out with eels, would have had the same result.

(3) In rivers, growth is generally less rapid than in lakes. This may be explained in one of two ways: either the plankton in running water is less rich than in still water, or the resistance to flowing water demands an expenditure of energy which eels living in lakes do not have to face. The influence of moving water on growth has already been brought out by Goetsch (1927) in respect of tadpoles.

(4) In his study of lakes and pools in North Germany, Wundsch (1916) recognised the parallelism between the nutritive capacities of these waters and the growth of eels kept in observation tanks.

(5) An experiment by Pellegrin and Spillmann (1938) enabled them finally to establish that the influence of food depends equally on its quality and its quantity. The experiment was carried out in the Aquarium of the Jardin des Plantes in Paris. Into an empty tank, without gravel, sand, stones or vegetation for use as a shelter, were placed on July 7, 1937, about a thousand elvers which had reached the coast in March of the same year and measured on an average 8 cm. with a weight of 0·60 gr. On the 5th of July 1938, about a year later, there remained only 71 eels. All the others had been devoured despite the fact that they had been supplied daily with meat and other foods. The sizes varied from 9 to 25 cm. Certain of the individuals had, therefore, grown only a little, while others had trebled their length. From this date, events moved quickly. There were daily scenes of cannibalism : eels having swallowed other eels whole had the tails sticking out of their mouths, or had distended abdomens. By the 8th of September 1938, there were only 12 survivors. A month later, their number was reduced to 3, and on the 17th of October, after having killed one of its companions and devoured the other, the biggest of the eels, nourished directly and indirectly by the major part of the inhabitants of the aquarium, measured 32 cm. and weighed 55 gr. Being now on its own, the eel in question was now fed with meat and worms. Its growth continued rapidly, since it showed in 1941, after 2½ years of this new diet, a length of 47 cm. and a weight of 135 gm.

The eel died during the war without anyone thinking of its being measured again. All one can say is that, arriving at the French coast in March 1937, it belonged in March 1938 to group I, in March 1939 to group II, March 1940 to group III, and in March 1941 to group IV. Its total age was at this time IV + 3 = 7 years. It was probably a female. Its growth curve (Fig. 13) stands out from that of all the free eels. One cannot imagine a better example of the influence of food overshadowing all the other influences of temperature and environment.

BIBLIOGRAPHY

ANCONA, U. D' La croissance chez les animaux méditerranéens. *Rapp. Pr. Verb. Comm. Int. Expl. Medit.*, Vol. X, (Paris, 1937).

AUDIGÉ, P. Sur la croissance des poissons maintenus en milieu de température constante. *C.R. Acad. Sc.*, Vol. CLXXII, (Paris, 1921).

BAUDELOT, E. Recherches sur la structure et le developpement des écailles des poissons osseux. *Arch. Zool. exp.*, Vol. II, (Paris, 1873).

BELLINI, A. Expérience sur l'élevage de l'anguille en stabulation à Comacchio. *Bull. Soc. centr. Aquic. Pêche*, Vol. XIX, (Paris, 1907).

BERTIN, L. Recherches bionomiques, biométriques et systématiques sur les épinoches. *Ann. Inst. Océan.*, N.S. Vol. II, (Paris, 1925).

EHRENBAUM, E. and MARUKAWA, T. Über Altersbestimmung und Wachstum beim Aale. *Zeits Fisch.*, Vol. XIV, (Berlin, 1914).

FAGE, L. and VEILLET, A. Sur quelques problèmes biologiques liés à l'étude de la croissance des Poissons. *Rapp. Pr. Verb. Cons. Int. Expl. Mer.*, Vol. CVIII, (Copenhagen, 1938).

FIDORA, M. Influenza dei fattori ambientali sull'accrescimento e sul differenziamento sessuale delle anguille. *Nova Thalassia*, 1, (Venice, 1951) 9.

GANDOLFI HORNYOLD, A. Recherche sur l'age, la croissance et le sexe de la petite anguille argentée du lac de Tunis. *Bull. St. Océan. Salammbô*, No. 17, (Tunis, 1930). Observations sur l'Anguille du Caumasée, *Bull. Suisse. Pêche Pisc.*, Vol. XXIII, (1932. La longévité de l'Anguille en liberté et en captivité. *Bull. Soc. Nat. Acclim.*, Vol. LXXVI, (Paris, 1935). *Vingt années de recherches sur l'anguille*, (Lugano, 1936)—containing a general bibliography of the works of the author. Observations sur le nombre de zones des écailles de 12 grandes anguilles de l'Etang de Berre, *Bull. Inst. Océan*, No. 725, (Monaco, 1937).

GEMZOÉ, G. Age and rate of growth of the eel. *Rep. Dan. Biol. St.*, Vol. XIV, (Copenhagen, 1906 [08].

HAEMPEL, O. and NEREISHEIMER. Über Alterbestimmungen und Wachstum des Aales, *Zeits. Fisch.*, Vol. XIV, (Berlin, 1914).

MARCUS, K. Über Alter und Wachstum des Aales, *Mitt. Zool. Mus.*, Vol. XXXVI, Hamburg, 1919).

MATISSE, G. Action de la chaleur et du froid sur l'activité des êtres vivants, (Paris, 1919). La loi d'Arrhénius contre la règle du coefficient de la température, *Arch. Int. Physiol.*, Vol. XVI, (Paris, 1921).

PELLEGRIN, J. and SPILLMANN, J. Inégalités de développement et cannibalisme chez l'anguille. *Bull. Soc. Cent. Aquic. Pêche*, Vol. XLV, (Paris, 1937).

SCHNEIDER, G. Über das Wachstum der Aale in den Gewässern Schwedens. *Pub. Circ. Cons. Int. Expl. Mer.*, No. 46, (Copenhagen, 1909).

TANING, A. V. A method of cutting sections of otoliths of cod and other fish. *Journ. Cons. Int. Expl. Mer.*, Vol. XIII, (Copenhagen, 1938).

TESCH, J. J. On sex and growth investigations of the freshwater eel in Dutch waters. *Journ. Cons. Int. Expl. Mer.*, Vol. III, (Copenhagen, 1928).

THOMSON, J. S. The periodic growth of scales in Gadidae as an index of age. *J. Mar. Biol. Ass.*, Vol. 7 (n.s.). (London, 1904).

WUNDSCH, H. H. Neue Beiträge zu der Frage nach dem Alter und Wachstum des Aales. *Zeits. Fisch*, Vol. XVIII, (Berlin, 1916).

CHAPTER IV

Euryhalinity and Toxicity

Two aspects of the physiology of the eel are particularly closely related to its mode of existence. The first is its *euryhalinity*, meaning its resistance to the variations in the salinity of its environment. This allows it to pass without injury from freshwater to sea water and *vice versa* in the course of its migrations. The second is its *toxicity* which, it seems, gives it a general resistance to morbid factors.

OSMOTIC PHENOMENA

Let us first remind ourselves of the nature of the phenomenon known to physicists and biologists as osmosis. It was Dutrochet who, at the beginning of the last century, brought it to light with the aid of his osmometer, a very simple apparatus consisting of a glass tube enlarged at the base and closed by a permeable membrane. The apparatus was partly filled with a sugar solution and plunged into a vessel of pure water so that the levels inside and outside the tube were the same (Fig. 15). The liquid was seen to rise slowly in the tube, attaining in a few hours a height (*II*) after which it fell until the previous level was attained. The incoming current or *endosmosis* was succeeded by an outgoing current or *exosmosis*. At the end of the experiment, the concentration was found to be the same on the two sides of the membrane. There was, therefore an influx of fresh water into the tube and an outflow of sugar solution.

At the moment when the liquid attains its greatest height in the tube, this height H is a measure of the osmotic pressure of the solution in relation to pure water. The stronger the concentration, the greater the osmotic pressure. If a sugar solution

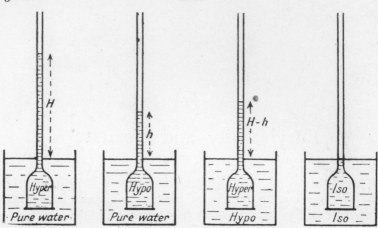

FIG. 15. Osmotic principles demonstrated with Dutrochet's osmometer.

The height *H*, *h*, or *H*—*h* of the liquid column measures the difference in osmotic pressure between the solution inside the osmometer and the pure water or other solution into which it is plunged. If the internal and external solutions are isotonic (as on the right) no osmosis takes place.

attracted the pure water only so as to reach a smaller height *h*, it would show itself to be less concentrated, or *hypotonic* in relation to it; whereas the stronger fluid is said to be *hypertonic* in relation to the weaker.

Let us now put into the osmometer a *hypertonic* solution and outside it a *hypotonic* solution. The height of the rising fluid is equal to the difference *H*—*h* between the separate osmotic pressures of the two solutions in relation to water. Finally, if we put the same solution inside as outside, if, that is, we use a pair of *isotonic* solutions, the osmosis does not take place. It happens only between solutions which are of different concentrations, i.e. are *heterotonic*. We can therefore define osmosis as an *exchange of solvent and solute between two solutions which, previously heterotonic, become finally isotonic.*

In fact, the osmotic pressure is only proportional to the mass concentration for the non-electrolytic *crystalloids*, such as sugar. When such a substance enters into solution, its molecules separate simply and completely one from another. But if we have to deal with a crystalloid which is at the same time an electrolyte, such as sodium chloride (common salt), not only do the molecules separate in solution, but a certain variable number break up into ions of chlorine and ions of sodium. The concentration of the particles (molecules and ions) which is what conditions the osmotic pressure, is not proportional to the molecular or " mass " concentration, but is higher. Finally, had one put into solution a *colloid* such as the white of egg, then the molecules, instead of disintegrating would remain associated in more or less large particles, so that the osmotic pressure would be less than proportional to the mass concentration.

Briefly then, for the same concentration by weight the pressure will be less strong for a colloid than for a crystalloid and less strong for a non-electrolyte than for an electrolyte. This will help us to interpret the phenomena of osmotic equilibrium.

It is inconvenient and not very precise to measure the osmotic pressure of a solution in the way shown above. Fortunately there is another method of assessing it, which consists of evaluating the depression of the freezing point of the solution in relation to pure water; because this latter phenomenon is due to exactly parallel causes. This degree of depression is represented by the Greek letter Δ. The instrument by which it is obtained is the *cryoscope* of which there are some extremely efficient models. For each substance, such as sodium chloride, we can construct a table giving the relation between Δ and the percentage mass concentration.

TABLE VII

Δ	NaCl per 1,000	Remarks	Δ	NaCl per 1,000	Remarks
−0·02°C	nil	Fresh water	−1·20°C	20	
−0·30°C	5		−1·50°C	25	
−0·42°C	7	Physiological	−1·80°C	30	
−0·60°C	10	saline	−2·10°C	35	Atlantic water
−0·90°C	15		−2·25°C	38	Mediterranean

STENOHALINE AND EURYHALINE FISHES

The significance of the above is that a fish can be compared to an osmometer in which the contents are the " internal environment " meaning the blood, the lymph, the bile, the urine,

E

the digestive juices, and so on. In practice, one may consider the blood alone as the internal environment and more especially the " blood serum " which can be extracted after coagulation. The fish is surrounded by its external environment which is either sea water, or brackish, or fresh water. For a marine fish in its natural environment, the internal environment is *hypotonic* in relation to the external environment, which is *hypertonic*. In other words, the blood is less salty than the water. The converse is true of a freshwater fish, in which the internal environment is *hypotonic* in relation to the external environment. How does it happen that the internal and external environment are not *isotonic*, or in osmotic equilibrium? This isotony is evident in the lower animals such as the sea-urchin; but in the higher animals and in particular the fishes, the cutaneous and branchial membranes, far from being absolutely permeable, like a parchment, are semi-permeable. These membranes have a restrictive and selective action on the osmotic exchanges between the internal and external environments.

Let us ask now what becomes of these exchanges when the animal goes from fresh to salt water and *vice versa*. This problem has occupied the attention of physiologists since Paul Bert. But is is only in the 20th century, as the result of progress in physics and chemistry, that the problem has been elucidated by the school of Paul Portier.

Duval (1925) compares the carp's reactions to changes in the environment with those of the eel. A carp invariably dies when it passes direct from freshwater to a mixture of half fresh and half sea water. On the other hand, it survives if the change is made by a progressive addition of salt to fresh water. In any case, it cannot tolerate a salinity greater than 15 per thousand. It is, as we say, *stenohaline*, meaning that it is incapable of going outside the narrow limits of salinity that its constitution imposes on it. The behaviour of a *euryhaline* fish, such as the eel is different; it appears to be unaffected by the rapid passage from fresh water to sea water, or back again, and tolerates wide extremes of salinity. For the eel, these limits range from those of fresh water to those of the higher salinities of oceanic waters. So it readily survives the differences in habitat met on its way to the Sargasso Sea, the same being true for the elver returning to inland waters.

Let us examine the osmotic reactions of the carp during experimental change of the environment (Fig. 16). Duval has established that the lowering of the freezing point of its blood serum changes from $-0·5°C$ to $-1·1°C$ when that of the surrounding liquid passes from $-0·02°C$ (freshwater) to $-1·1°C$ (a mixture of equal parts of fresh and sea water). In other words, the internal environment, previously *hypertonic* in relation to the external environment becomes *isotonic*, as it is in the lower animals such as the sea-urchin. It is different with the eel, in which the internal environment undergoes only a weak concentration and its Δ passes only from $-0·64°C$ to $-0·80°C$ while that of the external environment passes from $-0·02°C$ (fresh water) to $-2·10°C$ (sea water). Hypertonic at the beginning it becomes definitely hypotonic in relation to the surrounding liquid. It is as if the eel were almost able to resist osmosis. Its advantage, relative to the stenohaline fishes, compares with that possessed by birds and mammals with constant body temperature (warm-blooded), over those in which the temperature is variable with the surroundings (cold-blooded).

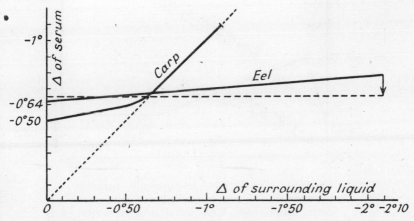

FIG. 16. Variations in internal osmotic pressure in a carp and in an eel kept in an increasingly saline medium (*after M. Duval*).

The works of Duval (1925) and of Boucher-Firly (1935) have established in addition, two very important facts:

(1) The euryhalinity of the eel is due to the slimy mucus with which it is covered, and it is this which forms the obstacle to osmotic exchanges. Eels dried with a cloth are as vulnerable as carp.

(2) This euryhalinity increases with age up to the moment when it is about to leave the fresh water for its great journey towards the Sargasso Sea. This can be demonstrated by following day by day the variations in the osmotic pressure of the blood serum in eels passing from fresh water to sea water (Fig. 17). At the end of 12 days, the difference between the lowered freezing point and its first value is still equal to 0·3°C in the small yellow eel of undifferentiated sex, to 0·15°C in the small female yellow eels, to 0·07°C in the large female yellow eels, and it is no more than 0·01°C in the female silvery eels. They have

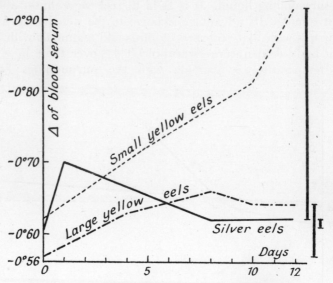

FIG. 17.   Variations in internal osmotic pressure during twelve consecutive days after being moved from fresh water into sea water.

The proportionate increase in pressure over the period (black scales on right) is the smaller according as the eels are older (*after S. Boucher-Firly*).

therefore regained in a few days the osmotic pressure they had in freshwater.

THE MECHANISM OF EURYHALINITY

Since the immediate effect of the passage from fresh water to sea water is an increased concentration of the blood, it is logical to think that the return of this pressure to its previous value is the result of an equilibrium established between the constituents of the blood. Now these are extremely numerous and varied. In the serum there are both minerals and organic substances in solution. The former are *chlorides, phosphates, phospho-carbonates, bicarbonates,* and so on. The latter belong to three categories, *carbohydrates* (glucose), *lipoids* (fats), and *proteins* (albumins, globulins).

The recent works of Macheboeuf (1936) and of B. Délage (1939), have shown that the lipoids are not in the free state, but associated with the proteins in the form of complexes, which some call *cenapses* and others, more simply, *lipoproteins.* What becomes of these divers constituents of the blood when eels, passing suddenly or by easy stages from fresh to sea water, adapt themselves to the new surroundings?

(1) The quantity of chloride increases as the result of the penetration of sodium chloride through the integument. The NaCl content was 6 to 7 per thousand in fresh water; it is 9 to 10 per thousand in sea water. The chlorination became hyperchlorination and, a curious thing, it stays so even when the osmotic pressure is reversed. We conclude that the hyperchlorination of the sea eel must be balanced by a diminution of concentration of other substances; to the " hyper " phenomenon must correspond some phenomena of " hypo " type.

(2) The quantity of phosphates is only slightly reduced, apart from a momentary increase, of asphyxic origin, at the moment of passing into sea water. Certainly it is not there that the compensating phenomenon resides.

(3) The quantity of bicarbonates undergoes a considerable reduction. These are one of the principal alkaline reserves of the blood, and one can measure them by the volume of CO_2

7

liberated from a litre of blood in a vacuum. In course of the adaptation, this volume drops from 500 c.c. to 200 c.c.

(4) The quantity of glucose is practically unchanged.

(5) The same is true for the urea.

(6) The quantity of proteins or, more precisely, of lipo-proteins, is notably reduced.

We can, therefore, suspect from this that the increase in the chlorides is balanced by a reduction in the bicarbonates and the lipo-proteins.

The osmotic pressure of the blood serum, at all times, is the total of the partial osmotic pressures of its various constituents. In other words, the lowering Δ of the freezing point of the serum is the algebraic sum of the lowering of the freezing points due to the chlorides (Δ_1), bicarbonates (Δ_2) and lipo-proteins (Δ_3).

Δ can be measured directly with the cryoscope; then, knowing the concentration per thousand of the chlorides and bicarbonates, we can calculate Δ_1 and Δ_2, and Δ_3 is obtained by subtraction. Here are the results obtained for large silver females:

TABLE VIII

Eels	Δ Total serum	Δ_1 Chlorides	Δ_2 Bicarbonates	Δ_3 Lipo-proteins
In fresh water	−0·64	−0·41	−0·08	−0·15
In sea water for 12 days...	−0·65	−0·57	−0·03	−0·05

Thus, as was anticipated, while total osmotic pressure has resumed its former value, that of the chlorides remains high, while those of other substances, in compensation, are lowered. Such is the mechanism for chemical auto-regulation. But we must determine exactly what part is played by the lipo-protein complex. Since these are colloids with, therefore, a relatively weak osmotic pressure in any case, the reduction in their pressure, important as it is, would not suffice to compensate—even with the help of bicarbonates—for the considerable increase in the proportion of chlorides. But something else has been pointed out by Nicloux (1938), who observed that a certain quantity of water is " fixed " in the lipo-proteins and incapable of dissolving any substance. The disappearance of a part of the lipo-proteins liberates part of this and lowers by that much the total osmotic pressure of the serum. In short the regulation which is produced in the eel in the course of its adaptation to sea water can be divided into five phases:

(1) Penetration of chlorides from the sea water into the eel's blood;

(2) Raising of the osmotic pressure;

(3) Reduction in the bicarbonates;

(4) Reduction in the lipo-proteins and liberation of the fixed water;

(5) Lowering of the osmotic pressure.

Moreover, these phases are not successive but simultaneous, and in silver eels take about twelve days to complete.

The problem of the euryhalinity of the eel, as it has been presented and resolved by recent work, tends to make us think this fish is unique in its resistance to variations in salinity. But in fact, many other fishes, such as the stickleback, salmon, shad and lamprey, are euryhaline to the same degree and probably through the same processes. On the other hand, such euryhaline fishes merely show to a higher *degree* the common properties of all fishes: " We believe," writes Boucher-Firly, " that although the division of fishes into euryhaline and stenohaline is made as a matter of convenience, no considerable importance must be attached to it . . . The stenohaline fishes, like the euryhaline fishes, modify their internal environment under the influences of a changing salinity . . . It is not in the biochemical field that we must seek the true mechanism of adaptation to a changing salinity."

Where then must we look for it? Probably in a nervous mechanism as yet unknown and likely to be very difficult to discover.

TOXICITY OF THE EEL'S SERUM

" The operatives who handle and cut the eels up for the preserving industry know that the blood of these fish is poisonous. If their hands are sound, without abrasions, contact with this blood, thanks to the protection of an intact skin, will not be injurious; but the smallest scratch admitting the poison often takes on a serious nature, with inflammation, mortification, suppuration, sometimes œdema complicated by lymphangitis and infiltration ". Such are, according to Roule, the local effects, generalised subsequently in serious cases, of the penetration of the eel's blood through the skin. Only one other fish would cause a comparable injury, the moray eel which, like the common eel, also belongs to the order *Apodes*. But other toxic species in order include another of the *Apodes*, the conger, then the cat-fish, tunny, dogfish, torpedo ray or crampfish, skate, lamprey, and so on.

It was Angelo Mosso who, in 1888, discovered the toxicity of the blood of the freshwater eel, the conger and the moray eel. Struck by its acrid and burning taste, rather like the venom of a viper, he injected it under the skin or intravenously in different animals, such as dogs, rabbits and guinea-pigs. With all he showed that death occurred after a period depending on the quantity of blood or, more precisely, of blood serum injected. Mosso named the poison contained in the eel's blood "ichthyotoxic" since changed to *ichthyotoxine*.

The toxicity of eel serum has been the subject of numerous works in France, principally by Richet and Hericourt at the Faculté de Médecine de Paris, by Camus and Gley at the Collège de France, by Césaire and Marie Phisalix at the Muséum National d'Histoire Naturelle, Paris. From these a precise technique has been built up. First the blood must be taken aseptically from the heart or the aorta with the aid of a sterilised syringe. Then it is coagulated and centrifuged. The serum is rendered more easy to handle and less potent by dilution to a tenth in physiological saline. Finally it is injected intravenously into the experimental animal.

The toxic action of the eel's serum comprises several distinct factors apparently due to different principles :

(1) Neurotoxic action or poisoning of the nervous system. With a strong dose, 0·1 to 0·2 c.c. of diluted serum per kg. of rabbit, the subject shows violent convulsions and within a few minutes breathing ceases and this is followed by heart failure. After a dose one-tenth as strong, 0·01 to 0·02 c.c. per kg. of rabbit, the subject shows signs of paralysis and within a few hours breathing ceases and again there follows heart failure.

The lethal symptoms being the same indicate a neurotoxin acting in both cases on the medullary and bulbar nervous centres. It may be noted that there is no effect if the poison is taken through the mouth.

(2) Cytolytic action, that is, one which destroys the cells. It is possible that a lysis of the neurones is the cause of the neurotoxic action. Pettit (1898) showed, on the other hand, than an injection of eel's serum causes an almost instantaneous change in the tissues of the kidneys. The urinary tubes shows a particular hyaline or granular degeneration of their walls, the cavity becomes obstructed, and the urine contains blood (hæmaturia).

Linked with the cytolysis is a hæmolysis, or destruction of the red blood corpuscles with the liberation of hæmoglobin so that a hæmoglobinuria is added to the hæmaturia.

Camus and Gley prepared a series of tubes containing water more or less saline and added to each a drop of the rabbit's blood; in all the tubes where the solution was hypertonic in relation to the rabbit's blood (in practice, more than 6 parts of salt per thousand), the red corpuscles remained intact and retained their hæmoglobin. Where the solution was hypotonic, on the contrary, the red corpuscles swelled and burst, and their hæmoglobin was dissolved evenly in the salt water (Fig. 18).

The experiment was repeated, but adding to each tube a drop of rabbit's blood and a few drops of eel serum. Immediately most of the tubes became red, which proved that in a hypertonic solution, the red corpuscles are destroyed and the hæmoglobin freed by the action of a hæmolysin. A series of such tubes enables us to measure precisely the hæmolytic effect.

(3) An anti-coagulation action. The injected rabbit's blood loses its ability to coagulate. But Delezenne (1897) has shown that this is a question of indirect action. The eel serum in reality stimulates the rabbit's liver to secrete an anti-coagulating diastase with an action comparable to that of peptone.

ANTI-EEL SERUM

The work of Pasteur has accustomed us to the phenomena of immunity and immunisation, so there is nothing surprising

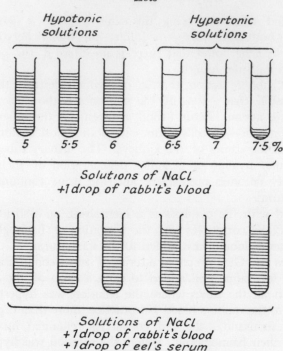

Fig. 18. Haemolysis tubes.

Without eel serum (upper tubes), haemolysis, freeing haemoglobin, takes place only in the hypotonic solutions. In its presence (lower tubes) it takes place in all solutions (*after Camus and Gley*).

in Richet and Hericourt (1897) trying to immunise against the neurotoxin of the eel. Their crucial experiment consisted of injecting a rabbit with increasing doses of eel serum until it became resistant to a dose which was rapidly mortal for a rabbit-control. It is possible to demonstrate that this acquired resistance is due to the presence in the blood of the vaccinated rabbit of an anti-neurotoxin capable of neutralising the neurotoxin—indeed this can be accomplished *in vitro*. It is sufficient to add to eel serum the " anti-eel rabbit " serum for a mixture to be non-toxic. The analogy fits perfectly with the well-known practice of immunising against diphtheria.

Can we also immunise against the hæmolytic action of the

eel serum? This new problem was solved in Germany by Kossel and in France, at the same time, by Camus and Gley (1898). The red corpuscles of a rabbit which has had repeated and increasing injections of eel serum end by resisting the destructive action of the serum. Consequently, if one admits that the eel serum contains a hæmolysin, the serum of the anti-eel rabbit must contain an anti-hæmolysin, just as it already contains an anti-neurotoxin. The neutralisation *in vitro* of the one by the other is proof of it.

Tchistovitch (1899) discovered another most curious phenomenon. If one continues to immunise a rabbit with increasing doses of eel-serum, it is found that its red corpuscles become more and more resistant to the globulicide action, but that its serum by contrast contains less and less anti-hæmolysin. For the immediate humoral immunity is substituted little by little a cellular immunity. Thus, repeated injection of the eel-serum imparts to the rabbit an adaptation which apparently spreads to all the tissues previously subject to cytolsis. Perhaps this adaptation is the result of a nervous reflex which, starting with the blood serum, comes back to the red corpuscles and increases their resistance by modifying their degree of permeability. The researches of Metalnikov (1939) showed the important part played by the nervous centres in the immunisation phenomena. Even the free cells of the body—red and white blood corpuscles—obey their directives.

Finally, it should be noted that cellular immunisation opens up immense perspectives in the matter of evolution. It shows, in a positive fashion, how a physico-chemical change in the internal environment can react on the tissues and modify their specific characters. It should not be forgotten that it was the experiments of Camus and Gley on eel-serum which, only half a century ago, initiated the more recent discoveries in this field.

A large number of animals possess a natural cellular immunity to the eel hæmolysin. In their zoological order these are the frog, toad, tortoise, viper, pigeon, chicken, hedgehog, bat, marmot and cat. The last two species are particularly interesting in having a resistance to the hæmolytic action linked with an extreme sensibility to the neurotoxic action. Camus and Gley deduced from this that hæmolysin and neurotoxin cannot

68 *Eels*

be one and the same substance. We can, moreover, weaken one without the other, or destroy them separately.

"TOXIC FUNCTION : TONIC FUNCTION"

Césaire Phisalix, well equipped for toxicological studies by his discovery, with Gabriel Bertrand, of the anti-venom serum, was able, in 1896, further to advance the knowledge of the toxicity of the eel. He found, first, that if eel-serum is heated at 56°C for 15 minutes, it completely loses its toxic power and can be injected into guinea-pigs or rabbits without harming them; furthermore, when its toxins, thermolabile substances, have thus been destroyed, the warm serum shows a very definite anti-toxic effect which was merely masked by its former toxic properties. Mixed *in vitro* with snake venom, it neutralises it. Injected into guinea-pigs it gives them, in a few hours, a more or less permanent immunity to snake-bite. It behaves, in short, as a natural anti-venom vaccine elaborated by the eel.

In 1926, Marie Phisalix demonstrated that the antitoxin effect of eel-serum enabled her also to neutralise *in vitro* the virus of rabies. The mixture of warm serum and rabies-virus can be injected into a rabbit by the most severe method (trepanning) without causing any damage. Injected alone into a rabbit, the warm serum gives it a relative immunity against rabies : it does not stop the disease developing but it does retard it.

Thus eel-serum contains at least two antitoxins or antigens, one venom antitoxin and one rabies antitoxin, and it is possible, moreover, to destroy them separately by the action of heat, ultra-violet rays, infra-red, short waves, and so on.

These things are not peculiar to the eel. Césaire and Marie Phisalix have shown their existence in the majority of animals having a toxic serum. These can be divided rather arbitrarily into three groups : the first (hedgehog, eel) have a toxicity limited to the internal environment; the second (batrachians) have the internal environment and the cutaneous mucus charged with toxins; those of the third group (venomous snakes) have their toxins distributed simultaneously in their internal environment and in their venom.

A priori, it is difficult to see what use the toxins can be to the animals of the first two groups which, in the absence of organs for inoculating cannot use them for attack or defence. But the matter is clearer when one knows that the serum of these animals contains both toxins and antitoxins. The first have an excitatory effect on the nervous system, and perhaps play a part in the general metabolism. The second have a protective function against the internal toxins or those coming from the external environment (i.e. they are bactericidal). Thus, the animal with a toxic scrum possesses a means of defence denied to other animals: the toxic function is, for them, essentially a tonic function. " There, it seems, is its true biologic function, to which the use of venom with the aid of hooks, darts and stings, plays only an accessory role ". (Marie Phisalix).

Peyron (1939) has brought new evidence in favour of the aphorism, " toxic function, tonic function ". After studying the distribution of epithelioma and sarcoma in the vertebrates having a variable temperature (i.e. the " cold-blooded " vertebrates), he stated that these tumours were rare or non-existent in the eel, toad, adder, viper, and so on, which are precisely those having the more toxic internal environment. It is worth mentioning the results obtained by the use of cobra's venom, in very small doses, for stabilising cancerous tumours and rendering them painless.

As to the eel, it is not inconceivable that it is so resistant to starvation, asphyxiation and wounds of all kinds, merely because it possesses the toxic function to a very high degree. Its exceptional endurance, its untiring energy and its tenacity of life, which manifest themselves particularly on the long migrations would be sustained by the ichthyotoxin impregnating its whole organism.

BIBLIOGRAPHY

BOUCHER-FIRLEY, S. Recherches biochimiques sur les Téléostéens Apodes. *Ann. Inst. Océan,* Vol. XV, (Paris, 1935).

CALLAMAND, O. Recherches sur le systéme lipoproteidique du sérum des Cyclostomes et des Poissons. *Bull. Inst. Océan,* No. 771, (Monaco, 1939).

CAMUS, L. and GLEY, E. *Recherches sur l'action physiologique des ichthyotoxines,* Masson, (Paris, 1912). A collection of the notes published by the Authors since 1898.)

DELAGE, B. *Le système lipoproteidique du sérum sanguin.* Thesis, (Paris, 1939).

DELEZENNE, C. Action du sérum d'anguille et des extraits d'organes sur la coagulation du sang. *Arch. Physiol.,* Ser. 5, Vol. IX, (Paris).

DUVAL, M. Recherches physico-chimiques et physiologiques sur le milieu intérieur des animaux aquatiques. *Ann. Inst. Océan,* Vol. II, (Paris, 1925).

IBANES, O. G., and FONTAINES, M. Recherches sur les proteines du sérum sanguin de quelques poissons migrateurs. *Bull. Inst. Océan,* No. 679, (Monaco, 1935).

MACHEBOEUF, M. A. *Etat des lipides dans la matière vivante.* (Paris, 1936).

METALNIKOV, S. L'immunité d'adaption et l'immunité de défense. *Rev. Gen. Sci.,* Vol. I, (Paris, 1939).

MOSSO, A. Un venin dans le sang des murénides. *Arch. Ital. Biol.,* Vol. X, (Paris, 1888).

NICLOUX, M. L'eau des tissus. Nouvelle contribution a l'étude d'une "eau liée" aux protéides. *Bull. Soc. Chim. Biol.,* Vol. XX, (Paris, 1938).

PETTIT, A. Altérations rénales consécutives à l'injection de sérum d'anguille. *C.R. Soc. Biol.,* Vol. L, (Paris, 1898).

PEYRON, A. Sur la fréquence des tumeurs dans les divers ordres des vertébrés à sang froid et leur rareté dans les espèces venimeuses. *C.R. Ac. Sc.,* Vol. CCIX, (Paris, 1939).

PHISALIX, C. Proprietés immunisantes du serum d'anguille contre le venin de vipère. *C.R. Soc. Biol.,* Vol. XLVIII, (Paris, 1896).

PHISALIX, M. *Animaux venimeux et venins. Vol.* I, p. 543–565, Masson, (Paris, 1922).
Immunité naturelle de l'anguille vis-à-vis du virus rabique et action rabicide de ce sérum. *C.R. Ac. Sc.,* Vol. CLXXXII, (Paris, 1926).
Rapports entre les venins et le virus rabique. *Ann. Sc. Nat. Zool.,* Ser. 10, Vol. XIII, (Paris).
Le sens biologique de la fonction venimeuse. *Rev. Soc. Arg. Biol.,* Vol. X, (Buenos-Aires, 1934).
Vipères de France. (Paris, 1940).

RICHET, C. and HERICOURT, J. Action locale du sérum d'anguille. Sérotherapie contre les effets toxiques de ce sérum. *C.R. Soc. Biol.,* Ser. 10, Vol. IV, (Paris, 1897).

TCHISTOVITCH, T. Etudes sur l'immunisation contre le sérum d'anguille. *Ann. Inst. Pasteur,* Vol. XIII, (Paris, 1899).

CHAPTER V

Juvenile Hermaphroditism and Sexuality

THE old writings we have quoted show what a variety of speculation has been lavished on the subject of the reproduction of the eel. After having been denied all sexuality, it has been successively believed to be hermaphrodite, viviparous and finally oviparous, as in fact it is. A century separated the discovery of the ovaries by Mondini (1777) from that of the testes by Syrski (1874). It has taken over half a century to understand the development of these organs and to discover their juvenile hermaphroditism. Even today, the factors determining the sex of the adult are the subject of debate.

INITIAL PHASES OF DEVELOPMENT

The work of Grassi (1919), Mazza (1923), D'Ancona (1924) and, especially, Rodolico (1933) established that the development of the gonads of the eel is divisible into four phases, which can be called: (1) Initial phase of neutrality; (2) Phase of precocious feminisation; (3) Phase of juvenile hermaphroditism; (4) Phase of masculinisation or of definitive feminisation.

In other words, the gonads are first undifferentiated before becoming female, then both male and female and, finally, male or female as the case may be.

The neutral or undifferentiated phase is seen in elvers 6 to 9 cm. long and in young eels 10 to 14 cm. in length. On the dorsal wall of the coelom in these young specimens are simple swellings or genital crests which increase rapidly in height while becoming constricted and finally stalked at the base to form genital bands (Fig. 19, a, b), attached by a sort of mesentery to the body-wall. Later their free edges become undulating and lobulate. The genital bands then take on the appearance of lobulated organs or miniature Organs of Syrski.

From the histological point of view, these primitive gonads are composed of a germinal epithelium enveloping an internal mass of mesenchyme. The epithelium is no more than a differentiated part of the internal lining of the coelom. Under the

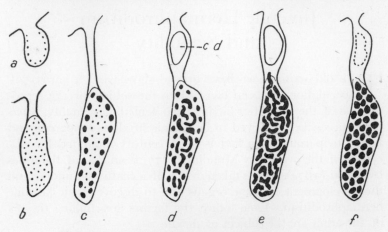

FIG. 19.   Diagram of sexual phases in the eel.

a, b, undifferentiated gonads; *c,* gonad with nests of oogonia in the cortex (precocious feminisation); *d,* gonad with nests of oocytes and strings of spermatogonia (juvenile hermaphroditism); *e, f,* definitely male or female gonads; *c, d,* vas deferens.

microscope can be seen ordinary cells surrounding the large hyaline cells with a large nucleus which will give rise later on, as shown in Fig. 22, to all the germ-cells. These large cells are consequently known as protogonia or archeogonocytes and an intensive budding of the epithelium does not prevent them from being distributed throughout the mass of the organ.

Rodolico (1933) remarked that the archeogonocytes are quiescent in the elver and start multiplying actively only in the young eel 10 to 12 cm. long. A little later, in individuals 14 to 18 cm., the first differentiation into sexes takes place. Of the gonocytes produced by the division of the archeogonocytes, those of the peripheral or cortical zone give rise to groups or 'nests' of oogonia (Fig. 19*c*).

It is, in fact, a feminisation which can become definitive, but which can also, as we shall see, give place to a masculinisation. We may speak of this phase as 'precocious' and 'transitory'.

In each nest, the oogonia pass through a phase of multiplication followed by one of rapid growth giving rise to large cells, the oocytes, up to 0·2 mm. diameter, with a nucleus 0·08 mm. diameter and a cytoplasm in which oily droplets are beginning to accumulate. They are embedded in a mesh of mesenchyme together with numerous adipose cells destined to nourish them. (Plate VI).

While this process of feminisation is taking place, the gonocytes of the central or medullary part of the gonad divide in their turn and form vermicular masses or strings of spermatogonia. By this time, the eels are 18 to 30 cm. long. The simultaneous presence of nests of oogonia (giving rise to oocytes) and of spermatic tissues in the interior of the sex organs shows that there is realised, in these animals, a state of intersexuality or juvenile non-functional hermaphroditism, the principal characteristics of which are illustrated in Fig. 19*d*. A noticeable feature is that a vas deferens (*cd*) has made its appearance in the interior of the mesentery which attaches the gonad to the coelomic lining.

Externally the lobes have become accentuated and there is a greater resemblance to the Organ of Syrski, typical of the silvery males. The tissues themselves are the centre of a multiplication followed by an increasing volume of the spermatogonia which little by little are transformed into spermatocytes.

Thus the production of egg-cells and sperm-cells keeps pace in the same glands. "The rhythm of oogenesis," writes Rodolico " does not seem to be influenced by the masculinisation . . . The presence of male characters does not prevent the formation of the oocytes." One may remark, however, that though the oogenesis starts at a length of 14 cm. the spermatogenesis does not start until after 18 cm. In trying to accelerate experimentally the development of the gonads by a natural or synthetic injection of hormone, one finds that account must be taken of this differential. It is because of this that Lepori (1946) obtained no results from his elvers of 6–7 cm. and that D'Ancona (1948) was able to hasten the maturation of the oocytes only in young eels of 18 to 27 cm.

F

DEFINITIVE ASSUMPTION OF SEXUAL
CHARACTERISTICS

Any eel 18 to 30 cm. long, that is 5 to 8 years old, is likely to possess both male and female characters, although it is as yet incapable of propagation. None of the sexual cells is mature, and the hermaphroditism is no more than potential and a temporary phase in development. Soon a curious loss of balance occurs between the sexual attributes. As the one accelerates its development the other atrophies. Hermaphroditism gives place to a definitive masculinisation or feminisation.

Let us first consider the case in which spermatogenesis predominates over oogenesis. Rodolico saw clearly, on a series of slides, the various stages in the degeneration of the oocyte nests. At the same time, he followed the development of the spermatic tissues into the seminal tubules which finally link up with the vas deferens.

In the walls of the tubes, the spermatocytes undergo the two classic divisions which comprise spermatogenesis : (1) A reduction division with typical leptotene, zygotene, pachytene and diplotene stages; (2) An equational division, which immediately succeeds the first and results in each spermatocyte being divided into four spermatids.

As a rule the development of the gonads in the male silvery eels has not reached this stage at the moment when they disappear into the sea. Complete sexual maturity has been only rarely observed, as in the eel taken in the straits of Messina and described by Grassi and Calandruccio in 1897 and the one fished in a Danish fjord and described by Schmidt in 1906. On the other hand, it has been produced artificially with hormone injection by Fontaine and his collaborators (1934–36), and by Schreiber (1935–37). Their remarkable experiments will be described in a later chapter (page 104). It is sufficient for our present purpose that they achieved a complete transformation of the spermatids into active spermatozooids. Fontaine and Tuzet (1937) have described this *spermogenesis* or ultimate phase of spermatogenesis and have pictured it in great detail (Fig. 20).

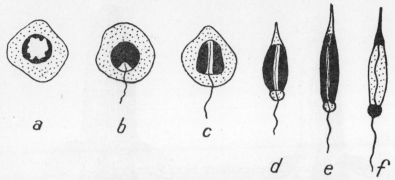

FIG. 20.   Phases of spermatogenesis.

a—c, spermatids; *d—f*, spermatozoids (*after Fontaine and Tuzet*).

As to the external morphology of the gonads and the changes they undergo in the course of masculinisation, some very precise notions have been obtained by biopsy, a method consisting of taking away parts of an organ at regular intervals in the same animal.   In the eel, a simple incision of half an inch just in front of the anus is sufficient for the removal of portions of the testes.   The operation properly carried out does not last two minutes and has no effect on the state of the subject's health.

One of the first results is an intense vaso-dilation.   Because of the inflow of blood the lobes increase in volume.   Their height ranges from 2 mm. in the hermaphrodite eel to 20 to 25 mm. in the silver eel; they also become whiter and firmer. There are about fifty from the anterior extremity of the testes (level with the pectoral fins) to their posterior extremity which is some distance behind the anus.   Near this is the urino-genital orifice where there open, besides the urinary duct, the vasa deferentia united in the middle line.   Plate II and Fig. 21 will make these points clear.

While such transformations are taking place in the male, others, no less important, are taking place in the female : the degeneration of the spermatic tissues, accompanied by the development of oocyte nests and the reduction and equational divisions of these.   Each oocyte is thus transformed into three or four cells, of which the largest is the ovum, while the others are the polar bodies (Fig. 22).

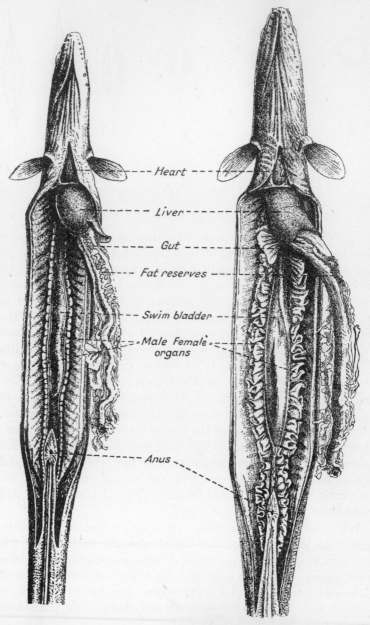

- - - Heart - - -
- - - - - Liver - - - - -
- - - - Gut - - - -
- - - Fat reserves - - -
- - - Swim bladder - -
- - - Male Female - - -
organs
- - - - - - Anus - - -

FIG. 21. Dissection of a male (left) and a female eel (right) (*after Walter*).

At the height of maturity, observed by Grassi in an eel in the straits of Messina, by Calderwood in an eel taken in the Channel, by Sulpino in an extraordinary eel in the aquarium at Milan, the ova attain about 300 μ (thousandths of a milli-metre) and are literally full of oil droplets. These are un-doubtedly derived from the connective tissue which has hitherto surrounded them and which has now almost completely dis-appeared (Plate IV, 7). In any case, full sexual maturity is never attained before departure into the sea, and no attempt to obtain it experimentally has been successful.

The greatest numbers of ova obtained were 5 to 10 millions. The eel is closer in this respect to the cod and turbot, which are among the most prolific fishes, than to the fresh water fishes, even the carp, the eggs of which are numbered by the hundred thousand.

These internal phenomena of feminisation are accompanied by profound modifications in the form of the gonads, which, from being lobate become pleated. Lepori (1883) was the first to discover this metamorphosis which was later studied by Mazza (1913). Illustrations 1 to 4 on Plate IV show how the lobes of the hermaphrodite glands come together, overlap at their edges and finish by becoming fused in a continuous band. The increasing length of this band in relation to its margin of attachment gives the characteristic pleated appearance to the ovary or Organ of Mondini (Fig. 21).

The vas deferens which appeared during the hermaphroditic phase begins to degenerate in the course of the definitive femini-sation. It is a character linked with maleness and which, as a consequence, cannot survive the change. One can trace a dif-ferentiation of its internal lining and the obliteration of its cavity. The silvery females have, therefore, no oviduct. It is probable that an increase in the volume of the gonads brings them into contact with the genital opening so that the ova pass out direct to the exterior. Such a method is not unusual in fishes.

SURVEY OF SEXUALITY

Let us look at Fig. 22 which shows, in diagrammatic form, the successive generations of the sexual cells :

(1) Above and to the right is shown the development from

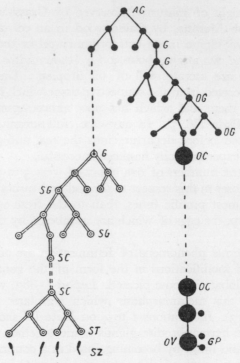

FIG. 22. Relationship of sexual
cells in successive generations.

AG, archeogonocyte; *G*, gonocyte, Polar
bodies; *OC*, oocyte; *OG*, oogonium;
OV, ovule; *SC*, spermatocyte;
SG, spermatogonium; *ST*, spermatid;
SZ, spermatozooid.

an archeogonocyte (*AG*), through the gonocytes (*G*) and the
oogonia (*OG*) to the oocytes (*OC*). It represents the sum total
of the neutrality phases and of precocious feminisation with
which the sexual development in all eels begins.

(2) To the left centre we see a gonocyte (*G*) having the
same origin as the gonocyte in (1), which gives rise to spermatogonia (*SG*) and later to spermatocytes (*SC*). Given that
these cells, grouped in the sperm cord, are present at the same
time as the nests of oocytes, the eel is obviously at this moment
in an hermaphrodite phase.

(3) Finally, bottom left, a spermatocyte (*SC*) completes its reduction and equational divisions to form four spermatids (*ST*), later becoming spermatozooids (*SZ*). This is the definitive phase of masculinisation.

(4) Bottom right, we see an oocyte (*OC*) divide into three cells, two of which, the polar bodies (*GP*), disappear while the largest persists as an ovum (*OV*).

The successive phases are of variable duration according to the individual. It may be recalled that individuals vary from 6 to 14 cm. in length for the neutrality phase, 14 to 18 cm. for the precocious feminisation phase, and 18 to 30 cm. for the hermaphroditic phase. It is to be regretted that the authors of works on the sex of eels have not expressed the age of their subjects as a function of the zoning of the otolith.

The hermaphrodite phase is remarkable in that it can be omitted or, on the contrary, be prolonged into the adult. It is absent in about 10 per cent of the individuals. In these, according to Rodolico, the definitive feminisation phase succeeds, without interruption, that of precocious feminisation : the male phase is suppressed. Conversely, hermaphroditism is sometimes apparent or latent in silver eels. Grassi has described a male whose well-developed lobed organs contained a mixture of seminal tubules and nests of oocytes. Many authors since Brock (1881) have affirmed, on the other hand, that any silver males prevented for one reason or another from going to sea, either died (which is the usual case), or changed their sex later.

On the whole, the reproduction organs of the eel seem to be essentially female, since they are precociously feminised and can return at any moment to the female type. The male characters are, as it were, secondary in the course of development. It seems that their status is always precarious.

GEOGRAPHICAL DISTRIBUTION AS A FUNCTION OF SEX

The obscure aspects of hermaphroditism and change of sex are subjects of prime importance in the study of the eel : is the definitive sex fixed at birth or can it be determined by the environment? It has often been suggested, in an attempt to

solve this problem, that the geographical distribution of eels is
a function of sex. The law is generally propounded as follows:
Males occur in the littoral estuaries and lagoons; females are
found in fresh water only. In proportion as one moves away
from the sea, the number of males diminishes and the number
of females increases.

Actually, there is about equal evidence for and against this
" law ":

(1) *Arguments for*: From an inquiry made by Gandolfi
Hornyold (1929) on the sex of the small yellow eel in Anjou,
it became clear (Fig. 23) that the percentage of males decreases
as one passes from the mouth of the Loire to its confluence with
the Maine. Tesch (1928) had already observed the same distribution in the lower Rhine and the Meuse (Fig. 24), and
D'Ancona (1935) in the lagoon at Venice. In the open lagoon,
nearer to the sea, the males predominate. In the " dead lagoon ",
which is nearer to the mouth of the Brenta, and receives in
consequence a greater amount of fresh water, it is the females
on the contrary that predominate. There may be from 35 to
80 per cent according to the salinities of the various pools or
intermediate *valli*. More recently still, D'Ancona (1946) arrived
at the conclusion that the *valli* nearest the sea produce mainly,
if not exclusively, male eels, while those more distant from the
shore, more difficult of access, or again those that receive more
fresh water directly from the interior, produce mainly, if not
exclusively, females.

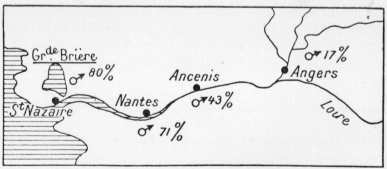

FIG. 23.   Percentage of male eels at certain points on the
lower Loire (*after Gandolfi-Hornyold*).

(2) *Arguments against* : In the course of his long and patient researches, Gandolfi Hornyold had on several occasions the good fortune to capture males at a great distance from the sea. He cites some records notably from the Tagus, at 600 km. from the mouth; in the Ebro at 700 km., and so on. In the Garonne, at Toulouse, he found only males. Another curious observation by the same author has particular reference to the pools in Languedoc. While most of them, following the general rule, contain 100 per cent males, the Étang de Vaccarès in the Camargue has only 45 per cent.

In the ports, Gandolfi Hornyold often recorded a majority of females. In Italy, Grassi and D'Ancona found that the lake at Porto has females only, while the lake at Orbetello, situated similarly on the coast between Rome and Leghorn, contains solely males. In Holland, Tesch obtained an average of 94 per cent of males in the Zuider Zee (the Ijssel Meer as it is now called) and only 70 per cent in the Waddenzee, nearer the open sea (Fig. 24).

It seems, then, that there are male and female localities and that their distribution can only be explained by one of the two following hypotheses :

First hypothesis : That sex is determined on fertilisation or union of the gametes (*syngamic determination*). The male and female elvers, when they arrive at the coast " choose " an appropriate habitat. Their different affinities cause some to move towards the brackish waters and others towards fresh water, while the greater muscular activity of some allows them to ascend the rivers for a longer distance from the mouth, and so on.

Second hypothesis : That sex is determined in the course of individual development and subsequent to the union of the gametes (*metagamic determination*). All the elvers that arrive at the coast are asexual and distribute themselves in a random manner. It is only much later that the environment in which they find themselves imposes one sex or another on them and can even cause a change of sex.

Let us see what the evidence is in favour of the one or other of these hypotheses.

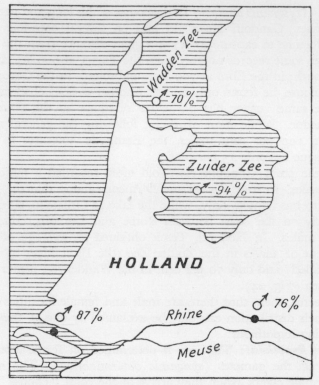

Fig. 24. Percentage of male eels at certain points in the Netherlands, before the enclosure and partial draining of the former Zuider Zee (*after J. J. Tesch*).

SYNGAMIC DETERMINATION OF THE SEXES

The syngamic determination of sex is the one most in favour with biologists since the discovery of the *allosomes, heterochromosomes, or sex chromosomes*, which differ in number and in kind according to the sex-cells in question. In the human species, for instance, the ovum, according to the latest researches, has 23 ordinary chromosomes and one heterochromosome (X). The spermatozooids have $23 + X$ or $23 + Y$ chromosomes and fall consequently into two distinct categories according to whether they possess the heterochromosomes X or Y. If an ovum is united with a spermatozooid of the first category, the fertilised egg so formed possesses $46 + 2 X$ chromosomes and will give rise to a girl. If the union, on the contrary, is with a spermatozooid of the second category, the fertilised egg will have $46 + X + Y$ chromosomes and will give rise to a boy, who will produce in his turn, on reaching maturity, two kinds of spermatozooids with heterochromosomes X or Y.

The numerous researches of Morgan, principally on insects, have established the undoubted value of the syngamic theory. It is natural then that it should be applied to the eel. But unhappily this animal constitutes, in the circumstances, the most intractable subject for study. First its ordinary chromosomes differ from one another in form and dimensions. Rodolico has counted 36 of them in his various preparations of sex-cells, but has not been able to discover, in this heterogeneous material, a chromosome that could be identified as a true heterochromosome. Secondly the eel is not amenable to experimental crossbreeding since it reproduces in the sea and under conditions that cannot be achieved in the laboratory. All that remains are the experiments that one can make starting with the elvers.

The first are those of Bellini (1907), who noticed first of all that the elvers arriving in the spring at Comacchio could be divided into three groups according to their length : 56 to 61 mm., 63 to 73 mm., and 78 to 84 mm. long. He then reared them separately in reservoirs especially established for the purpose in the interior of one of the pools or *valli* of the immense Italian lagoon. The result of his experiments was that the small elvers produced males only, the medium-sized elvers only precocious females, and the big elvers only backward females. Thus the sex and destiny of the individuals would be unchanged from the elver stage and probably from hatching. The determination of the sex would be syngamic.

In fact the experiments of Bellini gave rise to the most severe criticism from Schmidt (1906), Lübbert (1908), Hein (1910) and, above all, Orsenigo (1911). All these authors remarked that it is perfectly illusory to distinguish three groups of elvers according to their size. The polygon of variation that can be constructed with any sample of elvers—as for example, that made by Orsenigo with 500 elvers taken at the mouth of the Arno—is always a ' unimodal ' polygon, with only one summit, and not a polygon with multiple summits. At the most, one can say that elvers less than 60–65 mm. long, give a majority of males and longer ones a majority of females. The limits between these two groups are not precise and it seems that the determination of sex is not truly syngamic in all individuals. Rodolico came to the same sort of conclusion following his profound researches into the sexuality of the eel. According to him, 10 per cent of the elvers—the biggest and those which correspond to Bellini's third group—have the gonocytes more numerous and smaller than usual. If we remember that the elvers are at a period in which there is no multiplication of the germ-cells, it must be admitted that the abnormal number of gonocytes observed in the 10 per cent is the result of an anticipatory multiplication having taken place in 10 per cent of the leptocephali.

Here, moreover, are Rodolico's own words: " In the long elvers, the great percentage of small protogonia, that I have interpreted as an anticipatory multiplication present in the leptocephalus stage, could be an indication of a tendency towards a precocious acquisition of a large number of germ-cells. This makes it probable that effectively the long elver is already on the way towards assuming the female sex ". This precocity is again found in the succeeding phase of feminisation, in which 10 per cent of individuals—the same without doubt as previously—are more advanced than the others in their development and show more numerous oocyte nests more actively dividing. A little later still, at the end of the growth-phase of the oocytes, we can see that these immediately undergo their reduction and equational divisions which convert them into the ova. The sexuality of these females is acquired at a size of 15–25 cm. and without passing through the more normal phase of hermaphroditism. The gonads do not even show a transitory lobulation and merit at once the name of Organs of Mondini.

Rodolico explains in this way that many investigators could have discovered very small eels with readily recognisable pleated organs: eels of 24 cm. (Bellini), of 22 cm. (Grassi), of 21 cm. (Giacomini), of 20 cm. (Freud) and even of 15½ cm. (D'Ancona). Rodolico is, however, very cautious and even reticent in his statements : " I insist on the fact that I do not consider this phenomenon (of precocity) as an index of differentiation, but as a factor of sexuality, a factor which, under favourable conditions of temperature and feeding, would make the female sex predominate, but which in face of some adverse environmental conditions, would lose its determinant value."

To sum up, 10 per cent of the elvers and probably also of the leptocephali would have a precocious tendency to develop the female sex, but this tendency could be weakened under unfavourable conditions of the environment. No definitive argument in favour of the syngamic determination of sex can be drawn from the cytological researches of Rodolico. They carry no more conviction than the experimental work by Bellini.

METAGAMIC DETERMINATION OF THE SEXES

Can we arrive at more certain conclusions on the metagamic determination? The arguments are at least more numerous. There are, first, the cases already cited of persistent or latent hermaphroditism in the adult. We recall that a male silver eel prevented from entering the sea is capable of changing his sex and so adapting himself to life in a confined space. All this happens as if the sterility which affects the male elements makes possible a recrudescence of activity of the female elements. Mazza (1923) arrived at effectively the same result by the partial removal of the lobed organs in about thirty male eels in which he saw the gonads, by reason of the violent traumatism, developing in the direction of female organs.

Experiments of a totally different kind were carried out from 1913 to 1924, first by Grassi, then by his pupil D'Ancona. They began by dissociating the results obtained by Bellini from the interpretation usually given them in the syngamic theory. These results were : At Comacchio, in basins of many hundred cubic metres, where vegetation and plankton are abundant, where the temperature undergoes great seasonal variations, and so on, the small elvers gave rise to males, while the majority of medium-sized and large elvers became females. Is their sex determined in advance? Are we really sure that it cannot change under the action of the environment? Grassi and D'Ancona transplanted some large elvers into the tanks of the Institute of Comparative Anatomy at Rome. These tanks were of concrete and small, without vegetation and at a uniformly low temperature: precisely the reverse conditions to those at Comacchio: " Under the influence of these new conditions, the elvers, which, according to Bellini, would have developed almost exclusively into females, actually grew mostly into males ".

There is, however, one criticism of these experiments. Of the 250 elvers reared in 1913, only 69 survivors could be examined in the course of the succeeding years. The same rate of mortality continued to upset the experimental results, and there is no proof that this mortality may not affect one sex to the advantage of the other, the percentage of which would, thus, become higher (*selective mortality*). To this, D'Ancona (1924), replied that even when the individuals which died or disappeared were considered as females, the percentage of the males still remained much higher than in Bellini's experiments, and he came to the conclusion that: " In eels the determination of sex is easily disturbed between those truly male and those truly female; one can find all the intermediate stages. This gradation in the sex probably corresponds to a gradation in the length of the elvers, from the short male to the long female. In the intermediate forms, the external factors (including the limitations of space and perhaps also nutrition) can decide the sex in one way or another. The lobed organ must be considered typically as a testis, but can also, in the intermediate forms, become an ovary."

The same environmental action can result from the transplantation experiments carried out by Tesch (1928) and by Gandolfi Hornyold (1932). In Holland, as we have seen, the Zuider Zee or (Ijssel Meer) contains, almost exclusively, male eels (94 per cent). Tesch took small yellow eels from the Zuider Zee (then undammed) and reared them in a concrete reservoir in the Zoological Gardens in Amsterdam. At the end of three years, nearly half of them were females. The influence of captivity, temperature, food, and so on, had sufficed, therefore, to direct a certain number of hermaphrodites towards a sex which would have been inhibited in a natural state. The same experiment was made by Gandolfi Hornyold with the

eels of La Grande Brière, in which 80 per cent of the individuals normally become male. A hundred young, 20 to 30 cm.
in length (hermaphrodite phase), were put in a tank in 1928
at the Aquarium of the Jardin des Plantes in Paris. In 1931,
about fifty were killed and dissected, and in 1932, the eight then
surviving were killed and in their turn dissected. Of this total
about 17 per cent were males, 17 per cent females and 66 per
cent had remained hermaphrodite. The experiment is evidently
less clear than the one carried out by Tesch. It would have been
better to wait a little longer to know what would happen to the
hermaphrodites. In all cases, it is very probable that the definitive percentage of females would have been still higher than
under natural conditions.

More recently, Fidora (1951), and especially D'Ancona
(1951) tell of diverse experiments which show that the living
space given to the eels, as well as the temperature to which they
are submitted, are capable of turning them towards one sex or
the other. D'Ancona also lays stress on the action of synthetic
hormones in the evolution of gonads. We will return to this
problem when considering the sexual maturation of the eel.

The results from the habitual practice of repopulation can
convince us of the effect of the environment on the sexuality of
the eel. Every year, elvers and yellow eels are transported from
estuaries and littoral lagoons where they abound, to the pools,
lakes and upper tributaries of rivers, where they are of course
less numerous. In France the elvers of the Basse Loire and the
yellow eels of La Grande Brière are used. The Germans
formerly imported elvers from the mouth of the Severn. In
Holland, eels for repopulation are taken from the Ijssel Meer.
Now, all these innumerable individuals if left in their original
places would for the most part have become males, the more
widespread sex in the neighbourhood of the sea. Transplanted
to other places they give either an equal proportion of males
and females or a majority of females.

Therefore, an important percentage of young eels have male
as well as female potentialities. The slightest upset is capable
of directing these definitively towards one or the other sex, and
in this the habitat contributes a large measure. This being so,
can we say that we have reached a complete solution of the

problem? For that, one would have to know all the variations in the different factors of the environment, and of these we know very little. The difficulty of isolating them to study their actions separately is practically insurmountable.

A typical example of the complexity of the problem is found in the littoral pools of Languedoc of which only one, the Étang de Vaccarès in the Camargue, contains a majority of female eels. " It seems impossible to admit," writes Gandolfi Hornyold, " that the elvers which arrive at the coast choose this or that lagoon, according to their future sex. More probably, by its biological conditions, the Vaccarès determines a precocious differentiation in favour of the female sex." It is this biological condition which needs to be precisely analysed.

COMPARISON WITH OTHER ANIMALS

From all that has gone before it seems that the metagamic determination of sex—without excluding the syngamic determination in a certain number of individuals—is very nearly the general rule in eels. This was shown by (1) The juvenile hermaphroditism, or intersexuality, of 90 per cent at least of the young yellow eels; (2) The possibility of changing the definitive sexual direction by transplantation of young individuals into a new habitat; (3) The possibility of changing the sex of certain silver eels by growing them in confined spaces, by injury or other factors capable of causing a diminution in their present sex to the advantage of the opposing sex.

It is interesting to compare these facts with those which have been observed in other animals. Many fishes and amphibians provide in this respect excellent material for study. Okkelberg demonstrated in 1921 that American lampreys (*Entosphenus wilderi*) are all intersexes when young and that to tip the balance towards one sex or another a very feeble action of the environment is sufficient. Lubosch has found the same thing in other lampreys and in the hagfishes. The rainbow trout (*Salmo irideus*) behaves little differently according to Mrsic (1922). In one batch reared, 50 per cent of individuals developed directly into females. But the others passed through the hermaphrodite phase and later became males or females according to the circumstances. Here metagamic and syngamic determination exist together in the same species. Higher in the animal scale we find that in the alpine newts (*Triturus alpestris*), studied by Champi in 1921, males subjected to absolute starvation during the summer, at the time their spermatogenesis should be accomplished, undergo a complete fatty degeneration of their testes. When fed afresh in autumn, these old males develop into females and simultaneously change their external appearance; the crest is diminished in size, colour is lost and the cloaca takes on a new form. There is a total change of sex. " This observation ", writes Champi, " is clearly contrary to all theories of the pre-determination of sex ".

In toads the testes carry a structure known as Bidder's Organ. Harms (1921), on castrating some male *Bufo vulgaris*, found that their Bidder's Organs were transformed into ovaries. According to Guyenot and Ponse (1922–24), the organs in question are progonads inhibited in development and remaining undifferentiated, but with a female predominance. The same authors in 1923 grafted the testes of a toad on to the peritoneum or under the skin of male toads previously castrated. Testes so grafted became hermaphrodite : oogenesis and spermatogenesis were effected side by side in the same tubule.

Finally, the most celebrated experiments are those made by Witschi (1913–1930) on the common frog (*Rana temporaria*). These frogs comprise races differing markedly from one to the other in the matter of their sex determination :

(1) " Differentiated races " in which the sex is determined at birth. The tadpoles and young frogs are already male and female in equal proportion; (2) " Undifferentiated races " in which, as in the case of the rainbow trout, only 50 per cent of the individuals are from the outset female, while the others pass through a phase of intersexuality, and become female or male only as the result of external factors. Abundant food favours the development of females; a food deficiency on the contrary favours males.

The effect of temperature can be seen from the following : at 10°C. one obtains exclusively females; at 15–20°C. a mixture of sexes; at 27°C. males only. The rise in temperature clearly favours the development of males to the exclusion of females.*

From these results, Witschi supposes that the hermaphrodite gonad of the young *Rana temporaria* of undifferentiated races contains simultaneously two hormones: one cortical hormone (cortexin) and one medullary hormone (medullarin) respectively favouring oogenesis and spermatogenesis. This reduces the balance of the sexes to a balance of hormones, which, in turn, depends on the external environment.

The following diagram (Fig. 25) summarises the situation regarding the determination of the sexes. Each horizontal line represents the proportion (per cent) of individuals of unchangable sex (straight line) and of individuals of labile sex (dotted line). We see that the eel—accepting the proportion of 10 per cent fixed by Rodolico for the individuals of the first kind—occupies a position intermediate between the lampreys and the trout.

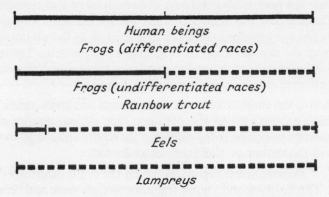

Fig. 25. Proportions of individuals with syngamic (continuous line) and metagamic (dotted line) sexual determination, in various vertebrates (*after A. Rodolico*).

In conclusion, the study of the sexuality of eels has brought us to the most modern interpretation of the concept of sex. Syngamic and metagamic theories have been invoked in turn.

---

* A thermal influence is seen equally in the distribution of the races: the differentiated forms are found only in Northern Europe, in the Alps and in the Pyrenees; the undifferentiated and the semi-differentiated in low-lying regions in Central Europe.

The syngamic theory is the oldest and depends upon the undoubted existence of sex chromosomes. The metagamic theory is the latest to arrive and is the more subject to debate since it depends on the phenomenon, found in an increasing number of animals, of juvenile hermaphroditism.

Can we reconcile the two theories? Let us note first that neither one nor the other appears to be applicable to all animals, more particularly to all vertebrates. It seems that we can distinguish three categories and that we can formulate the following hypothesis is respect of them:

(1) There are some *species without heterochromosomes* in which sexual determination would always be metagamic. This primitive state is met with in the lampreys, the hagfishes and other Cyclostomes.

(2) There are some *species with vulnerable heterochromosomes* subject to degeneration and subdivision under the action of physico-chemical factors. Certain sexual cells may, therefore, change their sex and the gonad become hermaphrodite; the final predominance of one of the sexes depending only on the metabolism and, indirectly, on the external environment. This gives the position realised in most fishes and amphibians.

(3) There are, finally, some *species with resistant chromosomes* in which the sex is unchanged from birth. To this group belong the human species and most of the higher vertebrates.

BIBLIOGRAPHY

Ancona, U. d' Sulla determinazione del sesso nell' anguilla. *Mem. R. Comit. Talass. Ital.*, Vol. CXI, (Venice, 1924).

Ricerche sul differenziamento sessuale delle anguille della laguna Veneta. *Boll. Soc. Ital. Biol. Sperim.*, Vol. X, (Varese, 1935).

Il differenziamento sessuale delle anguille. *C. R. XIIe. Congr. Int. Zool.*, (Lisbon, 1936).

Nueve ricerche sulla determinazione sessuale dell' Anguilla. *Arch. It. Oceanogr.*, Vol. III, (Limnol, 1943).

Observations sur les proportions des sexes chez les anguilles des lagunes littorales de l'Adriatique, *Dononaea*, Vol. XIII, (Brussels, 1946).

Prime osservazioni sull'azione degli ormoni sessuali sulla gonade dell' anguilla. *Rend. Accad. Naz. Lincei,* Ser. 8, Vol. V, (Rome, 1948).

Tentativi di deviazione sessuale nell'anguilla. *Boll. Zool.* 18, (Turin, 1951).

BELLINI, A.   Expériences sur l'élevage de l'Anguille en stabulation à Comacchio. *Bull. Soc. Centr. Aquic. Pêche,* Vol. XIX, (Paris, 1907).

BROCK, J.   Untersuchungen über die Geschlechtsorgane einiger Muraenoiden. *Mitt Z. St. Neapel,* Vol. II, (1881).

FIDORA, M.   Influenza die fattori ambientali sull'accrescimento e sul differenziamento sessuale delle anguille. *Nova Thalassia,* 1, 9. (Venice, 1951).

FONTAINE, M.   Sur la maturation complète des organes génitaux de l'anguille mâle et l'émission spontanée de ses produits sexuels. *C.R. Acad. Sc.,* Vol. CCII, (Paris, 1936).

FONTAINE, M. and TUZET, O.   Sur la spermatogénèse de l'anguille argentée. *Arch. Zool. Exp.,* Vol. LXXVIII, (Paris, 1937).

FREUD, S.   Beobachtungen über Gestaltung und feineren Bau der als Hoden beschriebenen Lappenorgane des Aals. *Sitzb. K. Akad. Wiss.,* Vol. LXXV, (Vienna, 1877).

GANDOLFI HORNYOLD, A. G.   Observations sur le sexe des anguilles. *C.R. Congr. Grenoble A. F. A. S.,* (1925).
Recherches sur le sexe et l'âge de la petite anguille jaune en Anjou. *Bull. Soc. Zool. France,* Vol. LIV, (Paris, 1929).
Le sexe, la croissance et la zone des écailles de la petite anguille jaune des étangs de Thau, d'Ingril, de Vic et de Vaccarès. *Bull. Soc. Centr. Aquic. Pêche,* Vol. XXXVIII, (Paris, 1931).
Le sexe de la petite anguille de repeuplement du Marais de la Grande Brière après un séjour de trois et quatre ans dans un aquarium du Muséum. *Bull. Mus.,* Ser. 2, Vol. IV, (Paris, 1932).

GRASSI, B.   Nuove ricerche sulla storia naturale dell' anguilla. *Mem. R. Comit. Talass. Ital.,* No. LXVII, (Venise, 1919).

LEPORI, C.   Il maschio dell' anguilla. *Atti Soc. Ital. Sc. Nat.,* Vol. XXVI, (Milan, 1883).

LEPORI, N. G.   Effetti nulli degli ormoni sessuali sulle creste genitale delle ceche. *Atti Soc. Toscana Sc. Nat.,* Vol. LIII, 1946.

MAZZA, F.   Risultati di ricerche anatomo-istologiche sugli organi genitali delle anguille d'acqua dolce e d'acqua salmastra. *Boll. Soc. Zool. Ital.,* Ser. 3, Vol. II, (Rome, 1913).
Resultati ottenuti dell' ablazione parziale dell' organo del Syrski nelle anguille gialle. *Boll. Inst. Zool. R. Univ.,* Vol. I, (Rome, 1923).

MONDINI, C.   De anguillae ovariis. *Mem. Ac. Sc.,* Vol. VI, 83 (Bologna, 1777).

ORSENIGO, L.   Intorno alla lunghezza delle anguilline di montata. *Boll. Soc. Lomb. Pesca Acquic.,* Vol. IV, (Milan, 1911).

RODOLICO, A. Differenziamento dei sessi ed ovo-spermato-genesi nell' anguilla. *Pub. St. Zool. Napoli,* Vol. XIII, (Naples, 1933).

SCHREIBER, B. Ulteriori osservazioni sull' azione di ormoni preipofisari sull maschio di anguilla. *Boll. Soc. Ital. Biol. Sperim,* Vol. X, (Naples, 1935).

SYRSKI, S. Über die Reproductionsorgane der Aale. *Sitzb. K. Akad. Wiss.,* Vol. LXIX, (Vienna, 1874).

TESCH, J. J. On sex and growth investigations on the freshwater eel in Dutch waters. *J. Cons. Int. Expl. Mer.,* Vol. III, (Copenhagen, 1928).

CHAPTER VI

Migration of the Silver Eel

IN the course of its sexual maturation, the eel undergoes a veritable metamorphosis throughout its organism and acquires, to put it broadly, a "migration livery" which is the prelude to its great reproductive journey towards the Sargasso Sea.

MIGRATION LIVERY

To the primary sexual characters linked with the gonads and the mating organs are very often added, in a great number of animal species, secondary sexual characters, which although linked with sex have no direct reproductive function. Such are the crest and the crowing of the cock, the antlers of the deer and the lion's mane. These characters are permanent. Others are seasonal and constitute a "nuptial livery", of which many examples are found in birds, amphibians and fishes. In the eel, the ornament is also seasonal, but belongs to both sexes equally and cannot, properly speaking, qualify as a "nuptial livery". We do not know, in fact, the use of this ornament in the depths of the Sargasso Sea, and it is better to speak of it, as suggested by Schmidt, as a "migration livery".

Gandolfi Hornyold, who made some statistical studies on the relation of age and size to the appearance of the "migration livery", found that the more precocious males become silvery in the course of their eighth year of life, the more tardy in their fourteenth year. In the females, the extremes are the tenth and the eighteenth years. As to size, the males fall between 24 and 51 cm.; the females between 37 cm. and a metre or more. The smallest male was found in Sardinia, and the two smallest females were discovered in the lake of Tunis and at Comacchio, all of which are southerly localities. Without taking account of the extremes and the exceptional individuals, we can say that, in a collection of silver eels, the individuals less than 40 cm. are males, the individuals more than 50 cm. are females, and those between 40 and 50 cm. may belong to either sex. The silver eel's skin is thiner and tougher than that of the yellow eel. The dermis presses tightly around the scales, which it is impossible to extract simply by scraping. The mucus is also more abundant and more viscous.

Four kinds of pigments are present in the eel :

(1) *Carotenoids*, yellow or red pigments, soluble in oil, and related to the plant carotins and xanthophils of which they are perhaps only a fixed form.

(2) *Flavones*, also yellow pigments, but possessing a green or blue fluorescence and soluble in water. It has been demonstrated that they are related to the vitamin B of growth. Fontaine and Busnel (1939) remark that the two fishes whose skins are richest in flavones are the eel and the stickleback and these are definitely the most euryhaline fishes. Is this simply coincidence?

(3) *Melanins*, brown or black pigments, insoluble, found in granules in ramified cells known as melanocytes and melanophores. These black substances result from the destruction of cell proteins, and can be considered waste-products.

(4) *Guanins*, or pigments derived from purine, white or yellow in colour, and generally in crystalline lamellæ contained in guaninocytes or iridocytes. They are also waste, but originate in the decomposition of the nucleo-proteins.

All these pigments are distributed, as Panu (1929) has shown, in two layers : a superficial, situated between the epidermis and the dermis, and a deeper one, situated at the boundary between the hypodermis and the muscles.

The migration livery is characterised by an extension and an accentuation of the dorsal and lateral melanism, and by an intensification of the guanin on the ventral surface. The eel which was greenish on the back, yellowish ventrally, both colours being dull, now shines with a metallic sheen. Its back and flanks become nearly black, somewhat bronzed, with a purple sheen, as are the dorsal and pectoral fins. The belly is a silvery white, and the anal fin slightly pink. It is no longer called a yellow eel, but a black eel, white eel or silver eel. In Tunis and in Italy it is called the black ear (*orechio negro*) because of the colour of its pectoral fins, which seem also to be larger.

With the maximum livery, obtained in an eel injected with hormones, Fontaine and Tuzet (1937) found that the guanin silvering is restricted to a ventral band running from the pectoral fins to the anus. This proves that the migration livery usually described is not the definitive livery clothing the animal at the moment of the sexual act.

The modifications shown by the sense-organs consist of a general increase in size. The nostrils are dilated, the lateral lines become more readily visible, and the eyes especially increase in volume and become very prominent. D'Ancona (1927) has shown that their diameter may be as much as doubled, which makes the retinal surface four times as great and the total volume eight times as great as in the yellow eel. This hypertrophy is conditioned by a marked hyperemia. On the other hand, the number of visual cells remains fixed; they simply diverge from one another in proportion as the surface of the retina grows. The result is that the latter must be less and less capable of light perception and that, on the whole, the enlargement of the eyes constitutes degeneration rather than improvement.

A priori, the changes in the digestive apparatus must be considerable since the eel ceases to eat from the beginning of its sexual maturation (in August) and continues in a very strict fast until the time it migrates. Schnakenbeck (1934) and Berndt (1938) have closely studied the consequent regression in the various parts of the digestive apparatus. First of all, the intestine shrinks and loses the few sinuosities that it had in the yellow eel. Its lining diminishes in thickness, and, becoming flaccid, sticks together in many places, which further diminishes the internal diameter. All the tissues become thinner and the cells as well as their nuclei diminish in volume (Fig. 26). A new phase begins with the fatty and granulose degeneration of the cell contents. Finally, to autolysis is added phagocytosis. The intestinal lumen is filled with a pseudo-tissue which is without doubt made up of epithelial débris.

Such, broadly, is the state of dilapidation to which the

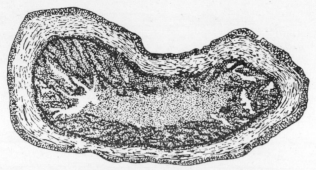

FIG. 26. Section of stomach, degenerate, in a
63-centimetre silver eel. (*after W. Schnakenbeck*)

digestive tubes of the silver eel are reduced. But many of the
details are of the highest interest and vary with different tissues.
The œsophageal epithelium of the eel is remarkable for the
variety of its cells. D'Ancona (1921) and Berndt (1938)
describe at least four kinds: some ordinary epithelial cells,
cylindrical, with hyalin contents; mucous cells, ovoid, reticulate
after staining with carmine and hæmatoxylin; club-shaped cells,
attached to the basal epithelium, with very refractive contents
staining best with eosine; and lastly taste cells, bunched in
groups and distributed throughout the mucosa even to the
entrance to the stomach itself.

This rich epithelium is reduced by auto-digestion to a histological poverty which is equalled in few other tissues. The
contours of all the cells disappear, the cells become undifferentiated; their cytoplasm degenerates into a granulated
syncytium in which the nuclei themselves finally become indis-
tinct. The same results are seen in the smooth muscle tissues.
The fibres are originally elongated cells in which the two ends
contain fibrils, and in the middle the nucleus surrounded by
hyaline cyptoplasm. Autolysis begins at the extremities and
advances little by little towards the centre. Muscle fibres at
different stages of dissolution are shown in Fig. 27. In the
striated muscles phagocytosis seems to dominate, prepared without doubt by the onset of autolysis. The white corpuscles
(uninucleate and polynucleate) can be seen to dissociate the
fibres and digest the fragments.

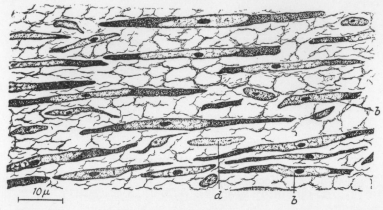

FIG. 27. Autolysis of smooth muscle fibres in the intestinal lining of a silver eel.

At the top, a complete fibre; *bb*, fibres with the fibrillary ends degenerate; *d*, fibre reduced to its central part and deprived of nucleus (scale, 1 cm.=10/1,000 mm.) (*after O. Berndt*).

In a silver eel taken in the North Sea, Schnakenbeck has observed the complete closure of the anus with a hardening and blackening of the neighbouring tissues. Although it might well be unique, this case is certainly not pathological. The parts obliterated do not present any morbid character and are associated with a genital papilla in excellent condition (Fig. 28). It is, therefore, possible that such anal occlusion may be a part of the normal cycle of metamorphosis.

From the physiological point of view, the silver eel is distinguished from the yellow eel by the greater rapidity with which it re-establishes in sea water the internal osmotic pressure it had in fresh water. The more perfect mechanism of regulation must be correlated with more highly-evolved nervous centres. This question has already been studied in a previous chapter.

The composition of tissues varies in its content of salt, water and fat. The following points have been brought out by Boucher-Firly (1935) and by Fontaine and Callamand (1940).

(1) *Salt-content*. The quantity of chloride in blood serum (chloremy) diminishes in proportion as sexual maturity is reached. The concentration of sodium chloride in proportion per cent may be compared with the gonosomatic ratio, that is,

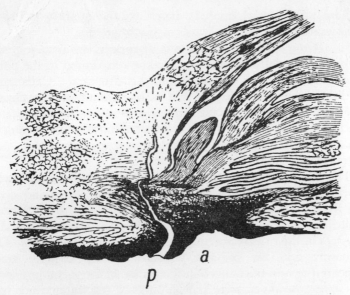

FIG. 28. Anal region of a silver eel taken in the
North Sea.

In this unique specimen the anus (*a*) is occluded, while the
genital orifice (*p*) remains normal. (*after Schnakenbeck*)

with the weight of the gonad expressed as a percentage of the
total weight of the body. Here are some of the results obtained :

Gonosomatic ratio	Salinity
0·46	5·6
1·24	4·9
1·35	3·6
1·55	3·0
1·63	2·7
1·75	2·0

Thus, a silver eel in which the ovaries represent about 2 per
cent of the weight of its body has no more than 2 gm. of
chloride per litre of blood and is distinctly hypochloremic as
compared with a yellow eel.

The demineralisation applies also to the muscles, progressing
as the time approaches for departure towards the Sargasso Sea.

Callamand's (1943) analysis, based on the quantity of solid residue after incineration, leaves no doubt on this.

(2) *Water-content*. As the salts disappear, the tissues apparently become dehydrated, then become rehydrated to the point where the eel is, in a way, hydropic (i.e. dropsical). Callamand attributes the restoration of the water-content of the tissues, after the stage of a certain gonosomatic ratio (about 0·13), to the fast to which the animal has been submitted, this leading to the raising of the ratio of cholesterine to fatty acids, thus favouring the resorption of the tissues.

The preceding results however have been called in question by Koch (1949). Studying yellow eels taken from lakes and silver eels from the neighbouring coast of the Baltic Sea, at the Danish aquarium at Charlottenlund, this observer observed no differences in their degree of mineralisation and dehydration. The chloremy and the osmotic pressure of the organic fluids appeared to him unchanged in the course of the metamorphosis. These eels, however, were kept in tanks of sea water which had a salinity of 3·5 per cent—which is more than that of the Baltic Sea. It is not surprising, therefore, that the eels, supposing that they had been previously demineralised and hyperhydrated when taken from their natural habitat, became remineralised and dehydrated in such an environment. The contradiction with the results of Fontaine and his collaborators is, in short, only apparent. Reference should be made to the outstanding review of this problem by Fontaine and Koch (1950).

(3) *Fat-content*. In the course of its life's growth, the yellow eel accumulates fat in its hypodermis, muscles, liver and gonads. Boucher-Firly (1935) and McCance (1944) noted percentages of 27 to 29 of fatty matter in silver eels. Vieweger (1928) had already supposed that the eel fattens exactly as a pig does, accumulating its fat for the most part in its muscular tissues; the eel certainly impresses the consumer as a fat fish.

What becomes of this fat during sexual maturation? The eel tells us little in this respect because it leaves the fresh water at an early stage of sexual maturation. Its gonosomatic ratio scarcely exceeds the figure of 2, while in the conger it attains the value of 30. Thus we can only infer from what happens in the conger what may take place in the freshwater eel. It is probable that the muscle fat passes into the blood, which drives it into the liver where it accumulates and finally passes into the gonads (especially into the ovaries), where it is used. It must be remembered that the oocytes and then the ova of the eels are embedded in a web of adipose cells which diminish in proportion as the fat reserves of the yolk are built up.

The lean flesh of the silver eel has a savour and a consistency appreciated by the gourmet. At Sète in Southern France the silver eels are called for this reason *anguilles fines* and it is these only which are exported.

Later on, in the Sargasso Sea, an ultimate degeneration of the tissues must occur. Cunningham (1891) has shown in fact that the skeleton of the conger becomes decalcified at the close of sexual maturity, and Perard (1930) gives the name of " rubber conger " to the animal which, with its flesh entirely denuded of fat and permeated with water, becomes practically uneatable.

DETERMINISM IN THE MIGRATION LIVERY

The naturalists of the old school claimed that if the eel becomes demineralised at the end of its life in fresh water, it is because it is going into the sea, which is a highly mineralised habitat; if the eel is dressed in sombre colours (apart from its ventral silvering) it is because it is going to live in dark or obscure water; if it acquires big eyes, it is to see better in a half-light, and so on. Grassi said that " the enlargement of the eyes must be related to the fact that the eel is going to live in sea water feebly lighted ". He saw evidence of this peculiarity in the eels found in the old sewers of Rome, called *chiavicarole* (from *chiavica*, sewer) which had enormous eyes but without concomitant development of the genital organs. Macrophthalamous eels are also often fished from wells.

But who can justify such an explanation of the characteristics of the silver eel? An organism cannot be what it is by reason of influences it has not yet undergone. In biology, the future cannot explain the present.

It is possible, of course, to shelter behind the prodigious phenomenon of heredity. It would be simple enough to say that

the eel changes to a silver individual because it is born of silver
eels, and only resembles its parents. But it would be a far-fetched
and lazy explanation. More and more, we must envisage the
development of an individual as a chain of partial developments
each of which determines the next. All embryology is "causal".
We must, then, investigate what, in the sexual maturation of
the eel or at its approach, is the immediate cause of the various
changes studied up till now.

First there are some phenomena which are due to the prolonged inanition of the eel, such as its demineralisation and its
hydrophily; this last character being linked with the increase in
the ratio of cholesterine to the fatty acids. D'Ancona (1921) has
shown, on the other hand, that the yellow eel, experimentally
submitted to a prolonged fast, presents the same degeneration
of the digestive tube as in the silver eel. His histological preparations are comparable to those of Berndt.

At present, biologists are inclined to regard most of the
modifications which occur in an organism as the direct result of
its metabolism. The substances called enzymes, hormones and
vitamins appear more and more to play the essential role in the
evolution of individuals and species. It is possible to suppose,
then, that sexual maturation and the migration livery of the eel
are also under the influence of hormones. Rodolico (1933)
was, it seems, the first to occupy himself with the question, in
the course of his penetrating researches on the eel's sexuality.
He reared some males until they became silver, taking from
them, at regular intervals, fragments of testis. In this way, he
was able to establish the following facts:

(1) The appearance of the migration livery is later than the
appearance of the interstitial tissue of the testes.

(2) It is, on the contrary, contemporaneous with the beginning of sexual maturation. At the same moment the silvering
of the skin starts, the protrusion of the eye-balls, the vaso-
dilatation and the increase in the volume of the testes, the multiplication of the sex cells and of the seminal tubules, and so on.

(3) It does not seem to be influenced by external factors.

Thus, brought to the conclusion that the migration livery
resulted from the action of a hormone, Rodolico refused to
admit, without very good reason, that it originated from the

gonads or the interstitial tissue. He considered other glands of internal secretions, such as the hypophysis. Taken away prematurely from science, Rodolico could not himself seek to verify this hypothesis, but others after him have done so.

Evans (1940) followed the seasonal modifications of the anterior and posterior lobes of the hypophysis and found that the migration livery (silver coloration, exophthalmism) is always in direct relation to an increasing activity of the gland. Moreover, the mode of action of the hypophysis seems complex. It has, in fact, been demonstrated that it is a question of a chain of reflexes having its starting point in the visual organs: a nervous or optico-pituitary reflex making the hypohysis react to retinal impressions; a humoral or pituito-melanocytic reflex making the melanocyte react to a nervous excitation of the hypophysis. Concurrently with the excitation due to the genital and hypophysial hormones, there occurs, in the acquisition of the migration livery, an undoubted influence from the thyroidal hormone. Callamand and Fontaine (1942) have, in fact, established that the thyroid gland of the silver eel differs from that of the yellow eel in its greater secretory activity. Now, we know that hyperthyroidism causes an enlargement of the diameter of the eye in exophthalmic goitre in man. Harms has demonstrated, for his part, that the injections of thyroxin in some fishes (Gobiids) causes an elongation of the pectoral fins and a thickening of the skin. A great many other characters of the silver eel appear to be attributable to the same cause.

We add, finally, an observation made by D'Ancona (1951) on a silver eel kept in captivity for six months. This eel, 20 years old, 98 cm. in length, had a perfect livery, as well as a number of degenerative aspects of the digestive organs and an enormous development of the intermediate lobe of the hypophysis. Although its ovaries had not evolved beyond those of a normal silver eel, the author considers that it had made a further step towards final metamorphosis which would have taken place in the course of its journey to the Sargasso Sea.

SEXUAL MATURATION

The principal problem in the migration of the silver eel is evidently that of the sexual maturation which accompanies it.

Here again, the physiologists have applied their methods, attempting to shed light on the last remaining mysteries.

Injecting male eels with commercial hypophysary hormones (prolan antefisan) Schreiber (1935) found a rapid development of the seminiferous tubules and the appearance of active spermatozooids. Experimental animals have thus been taken to the stage of development of the male eel fortuitously fished in the Baltic Sea (Plate V).

From 1933 on, Fontaine* pursued at the Oceanographic Institute and at the Museum in Paris some experiments in which commercial hormones were replaced by urine obtained during the first months of a woman's pregnancy. We know that this urine contains numerous hormones and notably prolans A and B originating from the anterior lobe of the hypophysis. A few intramuscular injections of 2 cc. of urine suffice to start, at least in some individuals, a complete sexual maturation. Two male eels injected on January 16th, 22nd and 31st, 1935, and February 6th, 1936, are particularly typical in this respect since they emitted, on February 23rd and 24th respectively of the same year, jets of sperm such as the males in the Sargasso Sea must emit.

Here is the account of the event by Fontaine and Tuzet (1937): "From February 23rd one of the eels emitted in the aquarium little white masses more or less disaggregated, which, examined under the microscope, showed spermatozooids very clearly motile. The day after, another eel exhibited the same phenomenon. These two eels had both taken on, in the days preceding the emission, a very noticeable livery. The ventral part of the animals presented a median white band, narrow and very clearly defined. This rectangular band, of dull white, spotted in certain places by little reddish spots, was wholly different from the well-known silvering of the eel coming downstream. The flanks showed a dark greenish-blue coloration with a metallic sheen. The ano-genito-urinary papilla was considerably flushed and swollen with blood. The anal fin was equally flushed and red, as was the lower jaw. More, the habitual characters of the silver eel (enlarged and protruding eyes and elongated pectorals) were particularly accentuated.

* First in collaboration with S. and M. Boucher.

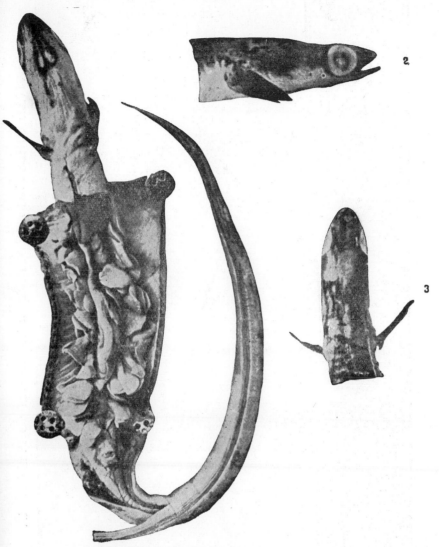

V   MALE SILVER EEL FROM THE BALTIC SEA

1. Dissection showing external development of testicular lobes.
2 and 3. Head showing remarkably large eyes (*after J. Schmidt*)

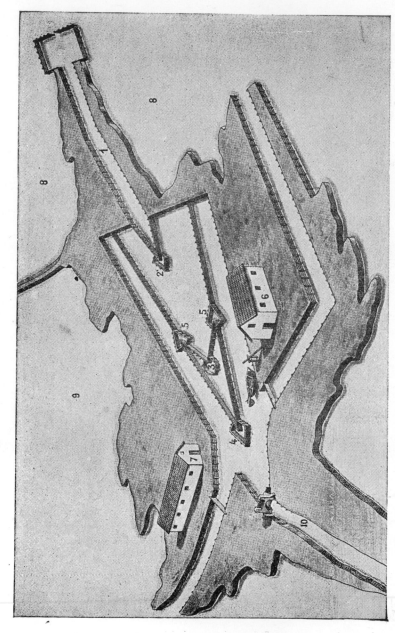

VI SYSTEM OF FIXED EEL FISHERIES AT COMACCHIO (ITALY)

1. Canal leading from the lagoon (valle)   2—5. Eel-traps, 6. Fishermen's huts, 7, Stores.

Twelve to twenty-four hours after the end of the emissions, the eels died." Such is the only portrait extant of eels at the moment of the sexual act.

The females showed themselves much more refractory to the hormonal action. Fontaine tried them not only with the urine of pregnant women, but with various extracts of hypophysis and thyroid with or without vitamin E. The only results obtained were a few modifications in the cutaneous silvering. Bruun, Hemmingsen, and Moller Christensen (1941–49) arrived at some perceptibly better results by intra-peritoneal injections of extract of urine from pregnant women and by simultaneous intra-musculary injections of a synthetic œstrogene hormone, Hexœstrol A. B. The diameter of the ova was brought to half a millimetre (500 µ), the biggest dimension observed until then, in the mature state, having been only 300 µ.

REPRODUCTIVE MIGRATION

With the coming of autumn, the silver eels leave the pools and water-courses in the interior and descend by degrees towards the mouths of the rivers; those which live in the littoral lagoons and the estuaries also reach the sea water. This first phase of their reproductive migration is called their descent or catadromous migration (κατα, down, and δρομοσ, course). The descending eels are often called in France *anguilles d'avalaison* (literally ' downstream eels ').

In most European countries, the descent of the eels is the occasion for a fishery distinguished both by its seasonal character (October–December) and by its pursuit of fish which, not taking nourishment, cannot be tempted by bait. It consists of establishing at the outlets to pools or lagoons, or across a watercourse, anywhere where the eels assemble to gain the sea, barriers which enable them to be caught in nets.

The *bordigues* of the French Mediterranean coast and the famous *lavorieri* (Plate VI) of the Adriatic coasts sometimes provide ten tons of eels in the course of a favourable night's fishing. The Étang de Thau alone, with an area of only 7,200 hectares, provides the fishermen with 70 tons each year, a weight equivalent to 300,000 eels. Five or six times larger, the

H

valli of Comacchio (Fig. 29) provide about 1000 tons, and the annual yield of the German fisheries of the Baltic and North Seas can be estimated at 2000 tons. Without adding to these figures, the importance of the autumnal migration on the European coasts as a whole can be readily appreciated. The exodus of the silver eels is certainly counted by hundreds or thousands of millions of individuals.

On the Severn in England the descending eels are caught in

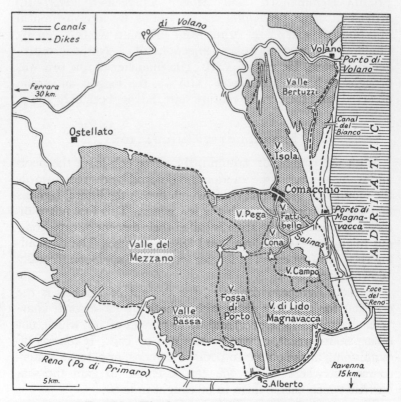

FIG. 29.   The lagoon of Comacchio, Italy.

This lagoon of some 80,000 acres (30,000 hectares) is situated between two branches of the Po delta, south of its main stream.   It is divided by dykes into valli (sing. valle) and for centuries has been used for the conservation of littoral fish (bass, mullet, sea bream, carp) and especially of eels.   The fixed fishing installations (*lavorieri*) are at the mouths of the canals debouching into the sea (see plate VI). Former valli on the north have been drained in recent years.

Autumn in funnel-shaped nets 50 ft. long leading to a narrow baited "cod" with a non-return trap; there is a good description in Bryan Waters: *Severn Tide* (Dent 1947).

The eels virtually disappear once they have reached the sea and we are almost completely in the dark concerning the tremendous journey of many thousands of miles which they accomplish in their passage to the Sargasso Sea. So far, it has been possible to observe them only in a few favourable places for the purpose:

(1) *Bosphorus and Dardanelles.* Berg (1917) and Hovasse (1927) recorded a migration from the Black Sea towards the Mediterranean.

(2) *Adriatic.* Grassi (1914), reported that the fishermen of Ancona, a town 200 km. south of Comacchio and Venice, observe every year during the autumn and winter months, columns of migratory eels going south. Numerous dead bodies are thrown by the winter storms on to the reefs at Monte Conero. Thus, the eels from the Adriatic head towards the Ionian Sea and through the Straits of Otranto. What becomes of them after, may be deduced: skirting the coasts of Calabria, they bear north to pass through the Straits of Messina in November–December, or at the beginning of the Spring.

(3) *Straits of Messina.* Grassi (1914) made full observations of them here, in relation to the fisheries at Reggio, Messina, Ganzirri and Torre del Faro. The principal passage takes place from November to December. The eels are best taken during the night, at spring tides when the currents across the straits are most violent and when the *sirocco* blows. Eels taken in these straits are more advanced in their development than those at Comacchio. Grassi found some males with active spermatozooids and some females with ova of 300 μ diameter.

At Comacchio there are two descents of eels, the most important from October to December, the other from February to April. At Messina also there are two passages, of unequal importance. Everything thus seems to indicate that the eels at Messina are emigrants, which, coming from the eastern Mediterranean, reach the western Mediterranean, the second stage of their migration towards the Sargasso Sea.

(4) *Baltic.* The Baltic Sea especially favours the study of

this subject. Shallow and not very salt, with an area of 150,000 square miles, and rather like a vast lagoon carved in the plains and plateaux of Northern Europe, it receives eels in their tens of millions every year, from the great rivers such as the Vistula and Oder, from the lagoons of the south-east margin and from the large Swedish and Finnish lakes. From all of these they converge towards the Sound, the Great and Little Belts and pass finally into the North Sea. Because it has been possible to follow their passage more easily, these silver eels, an invaluable source of food, are the object of important fisheries on all the coasts, which they follow in close columns in the course of their migration. Lundberg (1883) first noticed that the nets for eels must be directed towards the north on the eastern coast of Scandinavia, towards the east on the south coast, towards the south on the west coast. He also found that the fishery begins earlier at Grisslehamn (Sweden) than at Humbeleck (Denmark) because of the time the eels take to pass from one to the other locality.

Sufficiently interesting in themselves, these observations have led to some marking experiments made principally by Nordquist and by Trybom and Schneider (1908). Eels caught at the moment of their leaving the estuaries were marked with metal discs fixed at the base of their dorsal fins. On the disc was written the place and the date of marking. After release the fishermen were asked to help by recording all recaptures. Up to 30 per cent of the marked eels were recaptured after fairly long journeys, some of which are shown in Fig. 30, where it is seen that the place of recapture is nearly always nearer to the narrow channels of Denmark than the place of marking.

(5) *English Channel.* Calderwood (1893) was able to observe the nearly ripe ova of a female taken 20 miles south of the Eddystone lighthouse. Cligny (1912) received from a Boulogne fishing boat a dozen silver eels taken 20 miles south of the Cornish coast. There was, among them, a female of 90 cm., whose practically black migration livery, enormous eyes and voluminous ovaries indicated the approach of maturity. The fact that silver eels are not taken more often in the English Channel can only be due, explains Cligny, to the fact that they habitually swim well off the bottom, and therefore, out of reach of the trawls.

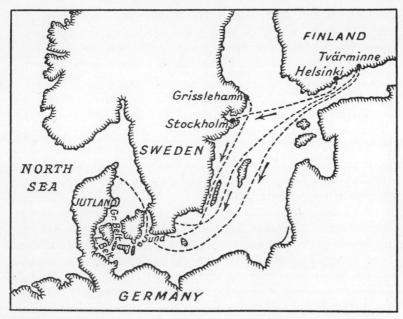

FIG. 30. Passages accomplished in the Baltic Sea by marked
eels which had been recaptured.

(6) *Atlantic*. The farther one goes from the European coasts,
the more rare become the captures; the only one taken in the
Atlantic, described by Vaillant (1898), was a silver eel found in
the stomach of a cachalot itself captured near the Azores, by
the Prince of Monaco.

Reverting back to the marking experiments, the speed of
migration can be estimated from the dates of marking and recapture, and the distances covered. In the examples given in
Fig. 30, speeds were from 8 to 32 miles per day, but it would
seem that this is a minimum imposed by the heterogeneous
nature of the Baltic Sea itself. Some local differences of
temperature and salinity, and especially the alternation of day
and night, compel the eels to make detours or to stop, thus
retarding their migration. The conditions of the journey in the
bosom of the deep ocean are another matter. There, total darkness and the small variation in physical conditions favour, no
doubt, daily distances of 30 to 60 miles. The eels leaving Europe

in October can, therefore, arrive on the spawning grounds at the beginning of the next spring. Moreover, the period of spawning is spread over many months, which seems to indicate that the breeding eels arrive successively and not simultaneously.

WHAT HAPPENS TO THE MEDITERRANEAN EELS?

One problem, among others, remains unsolved : that of the destination of the Mediterranean eels. We have seen that they pass the Straits of Messina in a westerly direction. But what becomes of them afterwards? Do they reach and pass through the Straits of Gibraltar to gain the Atlantic and continue their migration to the Sargasso Sea?

Not a single capture of silver eels has been made up to now in the Straits of Gibraltar, which are only 15 km. wide and 450 metres deep. Neither has one marked in the Mediterranean ever been caught in the Atlantic. Do the oceanographic conditions of the Straits constitute an obstacle to the passage of the eels from east to west? Let us examine the isotherms and isohaline curves around the subterranean threshold which rises here to within 500 metres of the surface (Fig. 31). While the tempera-

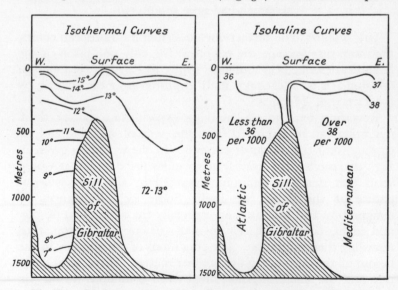

Fig. 31. Isothermals and isohalines in the Straits of Gibraltar.

ture of the Atlantic side falls regularly from the surface to the bottom, it does not fall below 12°C on the Mediterranean side. The curves of 13°C and 14°C rise from the east to the west across the Straits and mark the way a migratory eel could follow. There is, therefore, no obstacle from the thermal point of view.

As to the salinity, the right hand side of the diagram shows that the isohaline curves of 37 to 38 per thousand rise vertically above the sill off Gibraltar and continue to mount in this way until less than 150 metres from the surface before becoming horizontal again. An eel swimming in a depth of a few hundred metres, as must the silver eel, would therefore pass abruptly from water at more than 38 per thousand into water of less than 36 per thousand. This obstacle which would be insurmountable for a stenohaline fish, is certainly not so for a euryhaline fish. So neither on this account is there any hindrance to the exodus. The hypothesis formulated by Ekman (1932), that the Mediterranean eels remained prisoners within the Straits, can command no support. There is no factual basis for supposing that the Mediterranean is a huge eel-trap where, entering in the larval state, they must stay until the end of their days. There remains the hypothesis of a " Mediterranean spawning ". In the Mediterranean, it seems, the eels could pass through the whole of their sexual cycle. Grassi and Mazzarelli (1914) enumerate several 'deeps': one in the Adriatic, one in the Ionian Sea, one in the Tyrrhenian Sea, appearing to offer all the conditions of depth, temperature and salinity required for spawning. Yet the eel does not spawn there; specimens brought up have never included leptocephali of less than 50 mm. Schmidt's demonstration, that there exists only one spawning ground for all European eels, the Sargasso Sea, cannot be called in question.

In fact, it is probable that the Mediterranean eels do pass through the Straits of Gibraltar, but at such depths and at such times that they have so far eluded discovery.

MIGRATORY REFLEXES

Migratory fishes and birds pose the same problem. Under what impulse do they leave their normal habitat to make a long journey? Do they know where they are going? How do they orientate themselves? To invoke a migratory *instinct* is not an explanation—" the fishes and birds emigrate because they have the instinct to emigrate." This is merely to say, with Molière's doctors, that opium lulls to sleep because it has a soporific virtue.

As we have done with regard to heredity, we must analyse the migratory instinct into a succession of partial instincts which are finally broken down into 'reflexes' or 'taxes', that is to say, provoked movements, imposed and directed by the environment. Taxes* are not forces external to the animal, but its own reactions to excitations communicated to it, e.g. thermotaxis or the reaction to heat; phototaxis, or reaction to light, and so on. The animal is an hypersensitive reactor plunged into a constantly variable environment. The point of a compass in a magnetic storm is a fair enough analogy; incessantly, it orientates itself in search of an equilibrium never attained.

Now the yellow eel which has put on its migration livery and has reached its term of sexual maturity is an outstandingly impulsive organism the reactions of which we can classify under the following five headings : stereotaxis, rheotaxis, thermotaxis, phototaxis, halotaxis.

(1) *Stereotaxis*, or reaction to contact with solid bodies. The yellow eel is more especially an animal of the depths which likes to dig or lodge itself into natural shelters. But becoming sexually mature, it changes its habits and takes for preference to open water. From creeping, it becomes undulating. Roule (1937) puts forward the hypothesis that this coincides with a diminution in its specific gravity, due to a fatty infiltration of the tissues.

(2) *Rheotaxis*, or reaction to currents. As a consequence of what has gone before, the silver eel moves from the banks and the depths and reaches open water. At the time of the autumn floods the water is rapid and cold, and in addition, as Fontaine and Callamand have found, the muscular strength of the eel has slightly diminished because of its fast. It shows signs of debility and makes less effort to escape when captured.

* This term is preferable to the word tropisms generally adopted. A tropism in the exact sense of the word, is only a partial movement, the orientation of an organ such as the orientation of a flower towards the sun.

The coincidence of these external and internal factors means that when the full force of the current is reached the eel lets itself drift with the water; its migration becomes to a great extent passive. It seems quite natural that the fast should bring this diminution in muscular strength and passivity with respect to the current. In reality, the link between the two phenomena is not so simple. Fontaine and Callamand (1943) showed, in fact, that it is not so much the lack of nourishment which weakens the eel as the demineralisation of its tissues, consequent upon the fast. "It is well known", wrote Fontaine (1945), "that the demineralisation of the internal environment is accompanied by debility. If we made an eel fast in frequently renewed distilled water, which has the effect of hastening its demineralisation, we should see a debility appear in the animal in a few weeks, with a very perceptible lessening of the reactions to being captured, especially when accompanied by a fall in the temperature of the water. It is the autumn and winter floods which carry the silver eel towards the ocean. Such is the explanation which seems to us at present the most satisfactory, of the downstream movement of female eels ".

To prove that it is really the demineralisation which is the cause of the debility, Callamand (1943) took some nearly inert eels and immersed them in a saline solution and they revived in a few hours. Remineralised, they became extremely agile and rapid, and could not be captured by hand any longer. Let us return to rheotaxis. The study of the littoral pools shows that the out-going current carries the migrating eels. Roule (1937) made observations on the Étang de Thau and the canal of Sète which connects it with the sea. This canal is straight and runs from north to south. The wind from the south-east causes the sea-water to enter and the north-west wind causes the fresh water to flow out. Now, if the former excites them (as we shall see when dealing with halotaxis), it is the latter, and that alone, which assures the departure of the eels. Proceeding, therefore, from the rivers, or from littoral pools, the eels are guided to the sea by the out-going water. It is probable that other currents help them to leave the Baltic and the North Sea. Finally, having reached the Atlantic, Roule suggests that they are carried first by the Canaries' current, and later by the North-Equatorial current, and thus to the spawning grounds.

(3) *Thermotaxis,* or reaction to heat. Eels are normally much more active in warm water than in cold; active during the summer, they are benumbed in winter. This sensitivity to heat becomes more intense at the time of sexual maturation and in some way guides the silver eels during the winter towards warmer and warmer waters: from the pools towards the rivers and from there towards the sea, where, finally, they cross isotherms of increasing temperature until they reach those of 16°C to 17°C which enclose the spawning grounds. On the whole, thermotaxis acts in the same way as rheotaxis. The two reactions proceed simultaneously all through the journey.

(4) *Phototaxis,* or reaction to light. It has always been noticed by fishermen that eels make their catadromous migration by preference on the darkest nights. A beautiful starry sky, a full moon, or, moreover, fires lighted on the river banks, inhibit their movements. Often at Comacchio, the swarming mass of eels in the traps is so considerable, that the fishermen, afraid these will be damaged, light big fires in the neighbourhood, which immediately calm the fishes. Petersen (1906) chose a narrow and shallow river obstructed downstream by a sluice provided with a net (Fig. 32) and estimated, each quarter of an hour, the quantity of fishes captured. From 9 to 9.15 p.m., on a very dark night, 50 pounds of eels were taken. During the

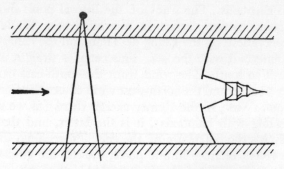

FIG. 32.   Inhibiting action of light on the catadromous migration of silver eels.

The beam of a searchlight considerably reduces the catch in a trap downstream.

following quarter of an hour, a shaft of bright light was projected on to the water. Immediately the migration ceased : the eels could not jump the light barrier, and only one pound were taken in the net. But when the projector was turned off, once again 50 pounds of eels were captured in a quarter of an hour. Petersen also used under-water lighting in the narrow channels off Denmark where eels pass on their journey from the Baltic to the North Sea, again demonstrating the inhibiting action of light on the migration. The impulse to shun the light must come into being by the time the eels reach the sea to make them go deeper and deeper, compatible with their need for warmth. In other words, the 'melting of the eels' as fishermen call it, must represent an initial plunge into the deep waters.

(5) *Halotaxis*, or reaction to salt. Those working the littoral lagoons know that they can quite certainly start the migration of silver eels by making the sea water enter the lagoons. Walter in his book *Der Flussaal*, published in 1910, writes : " They open the sluices to let the sea water in; immediately this exerts an exciting action on the eels and awakens their old migratory instinct; they precipitate themselves *en masse* and reach the traps which end their freedom ". Ignoring the use of the term 'migratory instinct', it is easy to understand that the demineralised eels are attracted and polarised by the salt of the sea water. However, it must be admitted that this chemical attraction has not been verified by experience. Silvest (1931) gave as an example some eels contained in a bucket with the choice of going to fresh or to salt water. He observed a complete indifference towards the one or the other. In any case, halotaxis cannot be compared in importance to rheotaxis or thermotaxis. Not only does it not affect the eels already in the estuaries or living in the littoral lagoons, but it is only an excitant in the matter of migration. The stimulus to make the journey would be without effect were it not for the currents flowing towards the open sea and leading to warmer and warmer waters.

To understand the successive reactions of the 'downstream eels' in the course of their breeding migration, one last problem must be resolved : that of the fate reserved for eels in enclosed waters. There are, in fact, pools and breeding reservoirs which do not communicate directly or indirectly with any river. What happens to the silver eels of these pools and reservoirs? In the first place, they do all try to go. Fontaine and Callamand (1941–1943) think that the excessive demineralisation and absorption of their tissues incites them to leave the aquatic habitat. It is then that they are seen wandering at night, in the damp meadows, profiting by their resistance to asphyxiation and desiccation.* But this excursion on to land is only temporary. Either their peregrinations lead them nowhere and they die, or they end up in a river which carries them away, or else they return to an enclosed water. Chance alone decides their fate.

There would be unbounded interest in a hypothesis which could, along with those above propounded, offer a comprehensive causal and physiological explanation of the catadromous migration. We can already perceive as causes:

(1) The demineralisation of the tissues following a prolonged fast.

(2) The absorption of the tissues because of the increase in cholesterine-content.

(3) The necessity for the eel to leave from an environment in which the balance of its hydromineral equilibrium is increasingly upset.

(4) The debility resulting from the demineralisation which brings with it a passivity in regard to water-currents.

The further aim should be to generalise this kind of explanation so as to be able to interpret each of the reactions of the eel in the light of its metabolism.

BIBLIOGRAPHY

ANCONA, U. D' Effetti dell' inanizione sul tubo digerente dell' anguilla. *Mem. R. Comit. Talass. Ital.,* No. I, (Venice, 1921). Ricerche sull' ingrandimento dell' ochio dell' anguilla in rapporto alla maturita sessuale e considerazioni sul suo significato biologico. *Rend. R. Acc. Lince,* (6), V, (Rome, 1927). Intorno alle trasformazioni dell' anguilla nella fase conclusiva del suo ciclo vitale. *Riv. Biol.,* 43, 2, (Perugia, 1951).

BERNDT, O. Morphologie und Histologie des Rumpfdarmes von *Anguilla fluviatilis* und die Veränderungen desselben im Individualzyklus. *Zool. Jahrb. Anat. Ont.,* Vol. LXIV, (Jena, 1938).

* See Frontispiece.

BRUUN, A. F., HEMMINGSEN, A. M. and MOLLER-CHRISTENSEN, E. Attempts to induce experimentally maturation of the gonads of the European eel, *Anguilla anguilla* L. *Acta Endocrinologica*, II, (Copenhagen, 1949).

CALLAMAND, O. L'Anguille européènne (*Anguilla anguilla*). Les bases physiologiques de sa migration. Thesis, (Paris, 1943).

CALLAMAND, O. and FONTAINE, M. L'activité thyroidienne de l'anguille au cours de son développement. *Arch. Zool. exp. gen.*, Vol. LXXXII, (Paris, 1942).

CLIGNY, A. Migration marine de l'anguille commune. *C.R. Acad. Sc.*, Vol. CLIV, (Paris, 1912).

EKMAN, S. Prinzipielle über die Wanderungen und die Tiergeographische Stellung des europaischen Aales. *Zoogeographica*, Vol. I, No. 2, (Jena, 1932).

EVANS, H. M. On some seasonal changes in the pituitary gland of the eel. *Brit. Med. Journ.*, (London, 1940).

FONTAINE, M. Quelques données récentes sur le mécanisme physiologique des migrations de l'anguille européènne. *Bull. Franc. Piscicult.*, Vol. XVII, (Orléans, 1944).

FONTAINE, M. and BUSNEL, R. G. Nouvelles recherches sur la répartition des flavines et de quelques autres pigments florescents dans la peau et les yeux des Téléostéens. *Bull. Inst. Océan*, No. 782, (Monaco, 1939).

FONTAINE M. and CALLAMAND, O. La chlorémie de l'anguille femelle au cours de son développement. *C.R. Ac. Sc.*, Vol. CCXI, (Paris, 1940).

Sur le déterminisme biochimique due retour à la mer de l'anguille femelle d'avalaison. *Idem.*

Sur certains facteurs des migrations de l'anguille. *Bull. Soc. Zool. Fr.*, Vol. LXVI, (Paris 1941).

Les aspects physiologiques d'une " vie cyclique " de l'Anguille d'Europe. *Bull. Mus.*, s. 2. t. XV, (Paris, 1943.

La fonction hypophyso-thyroïdienne des poissons dans ses rapports avec leur morphologie et leur comportement. *J. Cons. Int. Expl. Mer.*, 19, I, (Copenhagen, 1953).

FONTAINE, M. and KOCH, H. J. Les variations d'euryhalinité et d'osmorégulation chez les poissons. *Journ. Physiol.*, Vol. XLII, (Paris, 1950).

FONTAINE, M. and TUZET, O. Sur la spermatogénèse de l'anguille argentée. *Arch. Zool. Exp. Gén.*, Vol. LXXVIII, (Paris, 1937).

GRASSI, B. Quel che si sa a quel che non si sa intorno alla storia naturale dell' anguilla. *Mem. R. Com. Talass. Ital.*, No. XXVII, (Venice, 1914).

HOVASSE, R. L'anguille en Mer Noire et en Mer de Marmara. *Bull. Soc. Zool. France*, Vol. LII, (Paris, 1927).

KOCH, H. J. Quelques caractéristiques osmotiques de l'anguille femelle jaune et argentée. *Arch. Int. Physiologie*, Vol. LVII, (Paris, 1949).

McCance, R. A.　The chemistry of growth and the food value of the common eel. *Biochem. Jnl.*, Vol. XXXVIII, (London, 1944).

Mazzarelli, G.　Note critiche sulla biologia dell' anguilla. *Riv. Pesca Idrob.*, Vol. IX, No. 16, (Pavia, 1914).

Panu, A.　Les pigments du tégument de l'anguille. Thesis, (Paris, 1929).

Perard, C.　Le congre caoutchouc. *Bull. Biol. Fr. Belg.*, Vol. LXIV, (Paris, 1930).

Petersen, C. G. J.　The influence of light on the migrations of the eel. *Rep. Dan. Biol. St.*, Vol. XIV, (Copenhagen, 1906–8).

Rodolico, A.　Differenziamento dei sessi ed ovo-spermatogenesi nell' anguilla. *Pub. St. Zool. Nap.*, Vol. XIII, (Naples, 1933).

Roule, L.　La migration génétique des anguilles d'Europe. *Bull. Inst. Océan*, No. 733, (Monaco, 1937).

Schnakenbeck.　Veränderungen im Verdauungstraktus bei Blank-aalen. *Zool. Anz.*, Vol. CVIII, (Leipzig, 1934).

Schreiber, B.　Ulteriori osservazioni sull' azione di ormoni preipo-fisari sul maschio di anguilla. *Bull. Soc. Ital. Biol. Sperim.*, Vol. X, (Naples, 1935).

Sylvest, E.　Om Betydningen of kemotaxis og rheotaxis for glasaaleness Vandring. *Naturens Verden*, (Copenhagen, 1931).

Trybom, F. and Schneider, G.　Die Markierungsversuche mit Aalen und die Wanderungen gekennzeichneter Aale in der Ostsee. *R. Pr. V. Cons. Int. Expl. Mer.*, Vol. IX, (Copenhagen, 1908).

Vaillant, L.　Sur la présence de l'anguille commune en haute mer. *C.R. Acad. Sc.*, Vol. CXXVI, (Paris, 1898).

Vieweger, T.　L'influence de l'inanition sur la composition chimique des anguilles. *Arch. Int. Physiol.*, Vol. XXX, (Liège, 1928).

CHAPTER VII

Migration and Growth of the Leptocephalus

THE silver eel eludes observation once it has reached the waters around the European coasts. One cannot, therefore, follow the adult eels to discover their spawning grounds but is compelled instead to trace through the Atlantic their returning larvae. We must first discover their birthplace, then describe the spawning area and, finally, accompany the leptocephali in the course of their ' disseminative migration ', which coincides with their period of growth.

SPAWNING AREA

The discovery of this is one of the crowning achievements of Johannes Schmidt's work and took no less than fifteen years of exploration and investigation. Let us recall the essential dates:

In 1904, the discovery, west of the Faeroes of an eel leptocephalus 77 mm. long; it was the first larva of this species taken elsewhere than in the Straits of Messina.

In 1905 and 1906, the capture of numerous leptocephali, which had reached their maximum size, massing at the surface over the depths of 1,000 metres which fringe the European continent.

In 1910, the capture in the neighbourhood of the Azores, of larvae smaller and younger than those previously caught.

From 1911 to 1915, the capture of smaller and smaller larvae on the merchant shipping routes between Europe and the West Indies.

In 1913 the cruise of the *Margrethe* which, in the area between the Azores, the West Indies, and Newfoundland, discovered, at last, very young larvæ not long after hatching.

Finally, from 1920 to 1922, brilliant confirmation of these results by the cruise of the *Dana*, when Schmidt led his ship to the place of the spawning itself and followed the larvae, from year to year, in the course of their transoceanic migration.

The spawning area of the European eels is situated in the south-western part of the North Atlantic, between 22° and 30° latitude and between 48° and 65° longitude. Its central part is nearly equidistant from Puerto Rico and Bermuda. The ships which follow the route from Europe to the West Indies traverse it in the last third of their passage (Fig. 33).

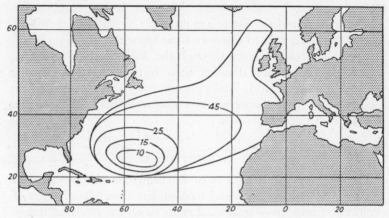

Fig. 33. Breeding area and dispersion of the larvae of the European eel.

The breeding area is that part of the ocean surface where are found larvae less than 10 mm. long. The diagram shows the limits attained in course of migration by larvae of 15, 25, 45 mm. and finally by those which are fully grown.

We often say that the eels spawn in the Sargasso Sea. This is not wrong; yet to be precise, the spawning area corresponds only to the central and deepest part of the region of floating seaweed. In general, a spawning area is defined by the presence of fertilised eggs and those containing embryos, which can be gathered in a fine net. The eel presents a more complex problem since we do not know, in fact, how to distinguish its eggs from those of other Apodes. The spawning area of the eels can be

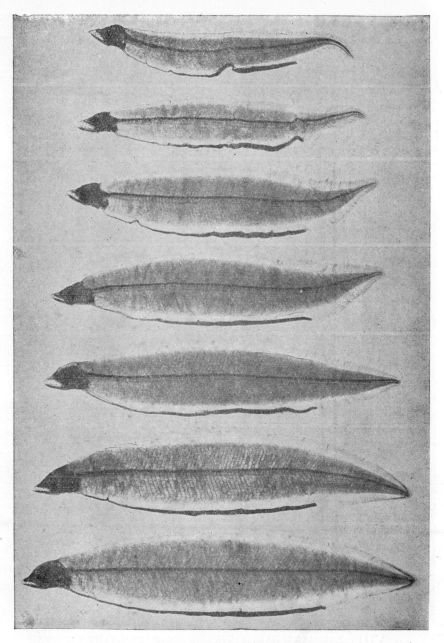

VII   EARLY LARVAL DEVELOPMENT
OF THE EUROPEAN EEL

Leptocephali of 9—24 mm, photographed by transmitted light
(*after J. Schmidt*)

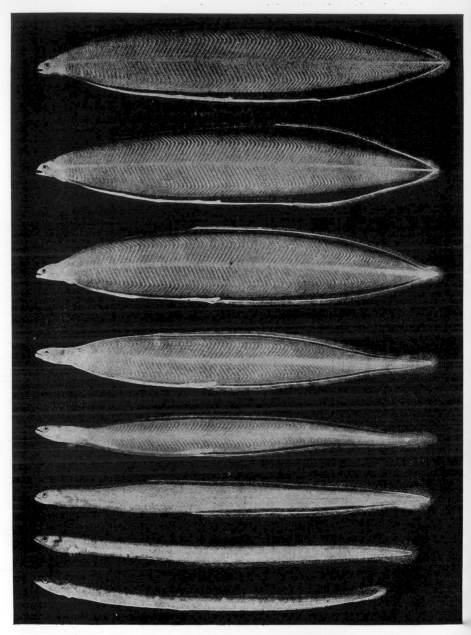

VIII   METAMORPHOSIS OF THE EUROPEAN EEL

Larvae **or** leptocephali at full development (above);   semilarvae
(middle);   and elvers (below).   Note the reduction in both length and
breadth (*after J. Schmidt*)

therefore, only the part of the ocean where the smallest leptocephali are found. The very small and slender larvae (prelepto-
cephali) cannot be far from the place where the eggs have been
shed and fertilised.

What are the oceanographic characters of the spawning area?
Before answering the question, we must know, at least, the distribution of warm and cold waters in the North Atlantic. A
book by Le Danois (1938) gives a good account of this subject
and also of its relation to the history of the Atlantic in the
course of geological time.

In the Secondary era, the Atlantic was reduced to its inter-
tropical part which was itself part of a marine-belt—what
geologists call the Tethys (after a marine divinity) or Mesogene
(the Greek form of " Mediterranean "). It stretched from the
West Indies to the Sunda Isles of the East Indies. This sea was
bounded to the north by a North-Atlantic Continent uniting
Europe to North America and to the south by an Africano-
Brazilian Continent no less vast. According to its fossil fauna,
the Mesogene was warmer and more salt than the seas of the
polar regions during the same epoch.

During the Tertiary era, the North-Atlantic and Africano-
Brazilian continents progressively subsided, and as a result the
cold and less saline waters from the north and south flowed
towards the tropics and, passing under the less dense mesogene
waters, mingled in the depths. This history is written in the
water itself since—as the section from north to south of the
Atlantic (Fig. 34) shows clearly—the warm and very salt
waters of the tropical Atlantic continue to form a bowl-shaped
mass quite distinct from the cold and less salt waters which
surround it.

To the north of the equator, the warm water basin is deeper
than in the south, and it coincides approximately with the superficial part of the Sargasso Sea. Its characteristics are as follows :
maximum thickness 800 metres, surface temperatures 20° to
27°C., temperature at a depth of 400 metres 16° to 17°C.,
salinity 36 to 37 parts per thousand.

The thermal maps drawn up by Schott, in 1902, following the
oceanographic expedition of the *Valdivia,* help us to specify
the limits of the European eel's spawning area in the interior

I

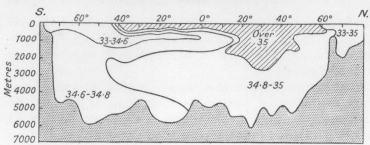

F ɪ ɢ. 34. North to south section through the Atlantic, at the longitude of the Sargasso Sea.

The isohalines clearly show the existence of a body of tropical water—the ancient Mesogene—quite distinct from the polar and deep-ocean water around it, and with a salinity exceeding 35 gm. per litre (*after E. le Danois*).

of the Sargasso Sea. That of the isotherms at a depth of 400 metres shows that the 15°C., 16°C and 17°C isotherms form concentric ovals situated exactly within the limits assigned by Schmidt to the spawning area (Fig. 35). More precisely still,

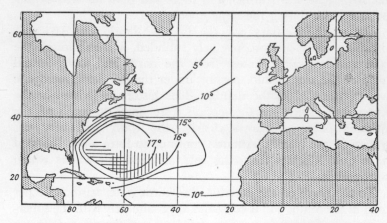

F ɪ ɢ. 35. Isothermals at 400 metres depth which limit the breeding areas of European eels (vertical shading) and American eels (horizontal shading).

the European eel reproduces, at a depth of 400 metres, between the isotherm of 16°C and 17°C in the area shown by vertical lines, while the American eel reproduces a little to the west, inside the isotherm of 17°C in that shown by horizontal lines. The two spawning areas thus overlap a little.

DEPTH AND DATE OF THE SPAWNING

At what depth does the assembling of the females and males, the spawning of the ova, the emission of the milt and the fertilisation take place? All these initial phenomena of reproduction occur out of sight and can be reconstructed only by collating a number of diverse observations.

(1) The eel belongs to the Apodes, a group of fishes most of whom inhabit the great depths of the sea. We may suppose, therefore, that the eel itself is a deep-sea fish that has temporarily strayed into freshwater and which, born in the sea at depths of about 400m., returns there at spawning time.

(2) The silver eels, (those in breeding condition) have precisely, as we have seen, the facies of abyssal fish.

(3) The ova that we have seen in the interior of the pleated organs contain numerous drops of oil. It is, therefore, probable that eel's eggs are 'floating' or 'pelagic' eggs and not laid on the sea bed.

(4) The same conclusion is drawn from the observation, in the very young larvæ (Fig. 36), of a rudimentary yolk-sac with oil-droplets.

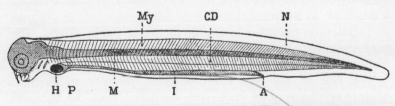

FIG. 36. Pre-leptocephalus of the European eel.

A, anus; *CD*, notochord; *H*, oily droplet in yolk-sac; *I*, intestine; *M*, spinal chord; *My*, muscle segments or myotomes; *N*, embryonic dorsal fin; *P*, pectoral fin. Length, 6 mm. (*after A. V. Täning*).

(5) The eggs of Apodes taken on oceanographic cruises have always been found, not on the surface, but floating at middle depths. It seems that the eel's eggs must in consequence be bathypelagic ($\beta\alpha\theta\acute{v}s$, deep; $\pi\acute{\epsilon}\lambda\alpha\gamma\sigma s$, high sea).

(6) In comparing the isotherm maps of the North Atlantic at different depths, we see that the isotherm of 15°C which, at 400 metres, bounds the oval space we have been discussing (Fig. 35), disappears at depths of over 600m. At greater depths the temperature is, then, less than 15°C and it does not seem possible that the eels find there favourable conditions for spawning. This must, therefore, be effected between 400 and 500 metres. It may be noted that this is precisely the limit of the penetration of light in the Sargasso Sea.

(7) When we consider that the bottom of this Sea is on the average 4,500 m. deep, we see that the eels, in the course of their reproduction, remain several thousands of metres above it and are rather pre-abyssal than truly abyssal.

(8) Though the eggs are fertilised at a depth of 400–500 m., the very young larvæ hatching from them rise to the surface without delay. Those which measure 5 to 15 mm. are taken for the most part between 300 and 100 metres. A little bigger and in consequence a little older, they are captured still nearer to the surface, generally at less than 50 metres. Making the analogy with an earthquake, one can say that under the sea there is a centre of spawning, fertilisation, incubation and hatching, with a superficial epicentre where the young larvæ assemble before being carried away in all directions by currents,

From March to July, the spawning area contains an immense quantity of young leptocephali. In one catch, in June 1920, at a depth of 50 metres, Schmidt took 800 specimens. In autumn and winter, on the other hand, the larvæ are totally absent. We may conclude, therefore, that the spawning period of the European eels is in spring and summer.

The fate of the eels after spawning presents an enigma. Mature eels have never been seen returning from the Sargasso Sea towards European waters. It must be presumed either that they die after having fulfilled their generative instinct, or that they continue their existence in the deep seas. A great number of facts support the first hypothesis:

(1) The degeneration of the organs of nutrition in the silver eels, de-differentiation of the epithelial, muscular and glandular tissues; and the anal obstruction observed in one specimen.

(2) The still more degenerate condition of the conger—a

near relative of the eel—at the same moment of its reproduction. It may be recalled that Pérard has described under the name of "rubber conger" some individuals entirely without fat and saturated with water. Cunningham, also, has observed that mature congers present a complete deterioration of their skeletal and muscular systems. Their decalcified bones have become soft and 'cheese-like' and their muscles are atrophied. The males, more affected than the females, have the skin ulcerated and the eyes so enfeebled that they are blind.

(3) The state of deterioration and the frequent mortality of other migratory fishes after the sexual act. Salmon for instance, are in a state of decrepitude and only very exceptionally survive. "The fish", writes Roule, "seems empty . . . elongated, thin, practically a skeleton; of an earthy colour, its bones covered with flabby flesh, softened, mucilaginous and covered by a frayed skin. It is no more than a shadow of its former self. A carrier of germ-cells, it has used its vital resources to engender and ripen them. The results attained and the germ-cells gone, all that remains of it is this organised shell, now deprived of its contents, this sheath still living, but from which life will not be long in departing. Carrion, we may call it, a brutal name but expressing a reality".

Why should the eels not have an analogous fate? Even supposing, as Grassi did, that they take some nourishment in the course of their migration, their immense journey can but have a fatal end. We have to think of the Sargasso Sea as being at the same time their tomb and the cradle of their offspring.

LARVAL MIGRATION

The eel larvæ form part of the extraordinary world of floating beings to which naturalists have given the name of 'plankton'. In all directions around the spawning area millions of leptocephali spread out. Those pushed north or south do not live long in the cold currents coming from Labrador or the warm currents of the equatorial zone. Those carried to the west by the currents arrive near the American coasts much too soon to be capable of metamorphosing. Having attained only a third of their larval development, they cannot complete it and die like the others. The only ones which have a chance to survive are the leptocephali carried in the Gulf Stream.

Wherever this current reaches, larvæ are brought in great numbers and the coasts are populated with eels (Fig. 33). Iceland and the Faeroes receive their contingents of European eels also. Now, these islands are in the same latitude as Greenland which, yet, because the Gulf Stream does not reach it, has no eels. There is not, perhaps, a more beautiful example of determinism in the geographical distribution of living beings.

A great deal has been made, for a score of years, about a discovery which seems in fact excellent: that of the North Atlantic Drift which, far from being a substitute for the Gulf Stream, as sometimes wrongly suggested, completes and amplifies it in the direction of the European coasts. While the Gulf Stream is a constant current which arises in the Gulf of Mexico and flows from it between Florida and Cuba, it is the warm waters of the inter-tropical basin which move, according to Le Danois, towards the north-east in the course of the summer and which attain successively the limits indicated by the accompanying diagram (Fig. 37). By contrast, in winter, they regress, while the warm waters of the southern hemisphere move in their turn. These movements of extension and retraction have been compared to diastoles and systoles, or better still, flow and ebb, having their fulcrum at the equator. They have a quintuple periodicity which Le Danois has correlated with a certain number of sun-moon phenomena. They explain, nevertheless, the seasonal displacement of fishes and allow us to forecast its range.

As to the migration of larval eels, we see that the North Atlantic transgression, which begins in March, precisely at the time when the young leptocephali are hatched, favours their displacement towards the north-east. The impetus which is thus given does not cease to be felt throughout their lives. In Fig. 33, the curve delimiting the extension of leptocephali in June is intermediate to those which delimit, in Fig. 37, the extension of warm waters in May and September. In other words, they are the same waters which, having assured the incubation and the hatching, transport the larvæ into northern latitudes.

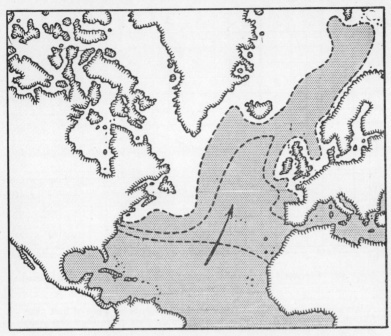

FIG. 37. Summer drift of warm water in the Atlantic.

Showing approximate limits attained in March, May and September
(*after E. le Danois*).

DURATION OF THE LARVAL LIFE

Let us consider the growth-curve of the leptocephali (Fig.
38). Month by month the average sizes of hundreds of leptocephali have been plotted against a graduated scale, then
joined by a continuous line. We see that an individual born, for
instance, in March 1950 and having a length of 4 to 5 mm. at
the time of hatching, was already 12 mm. in April, 20 mm. in
May, 25 mm. in June. Then its growth, at first very rapid,
slows down. It measures only 53 mm. in June 1951 and 75 mm.
in June 1952. In all, its larval development has lasted 2½ years.
So in June 1952 there are to be found leptocephali belonging to
three annual groups:

(1) Leptocephali born in March 1952 and having an
average size of 25 mm.

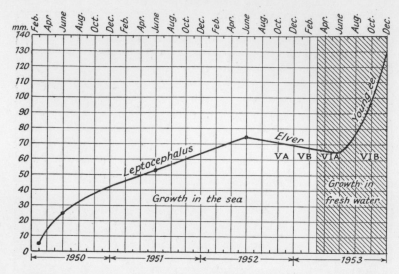

F<small>IG</small>. 38.   Growth curve of European eel during larval life and metamorphosis.

A larva born e.g. in March 1950 attained 25 mm. in June of that year, 53 mm. in June 1951, 75 mm. in June 1952, after more than two years' growth.   Its metamorphosis then began, with loss of length and weight until Stage VIA.   Fresh water was reached in March 1953 at the age of three years, and during that summer it began to grow again (*adapted from Schmidt*).

(2) Leptocephali born in March 1951 and having an average size of 53 mm.

(3) Leptocephali born in March 1950 and having an average size of 75 mm.

Schmidt called these, Group O, Group I, Group II. Group O contains leptocephali just hatched and beginning their larval development.   Group II succeeding Group I contains fully grown leptocephali about to metamorphose.   (To obtain the total age of an eel, these three years of marine life must be added to the number of winter zones on the otoliths.)

Given that the larvæ are nearing Europe in proportion as they grow, it is not surprising that an oceanographic ship, starting from the Sargasso Sea and following the route of the migration, should come across older and older leptocephali—Group O to the west of 50° longitude, Group I between 50° and 20°,

Group II to the east of 20°. Such, according to Schmidt, is the distribution of the annual groups in the course of the summer.

Actually, the results obtained by the *Thor*, the *Margrethe*, *the Dana* and the *Michael Sars*, are not so simple as this. First, the period of spawning extends over several months instead of being restricted, as has previously been supposed, to the month of March only. Then the various larvæ, for several reasons, have not the same rate of growth nor do they move at the same speed. It is not uncommon to capture in the same haul of the net individuals of different groups.

Schmidt overcame the difficulty by plotting on a map (Fig. 33) the minimum length of specimens caught in each locality. The curve marked e.g. 25 is the limit beyond which no leptocephali of less than 25 mm. could be found. On another map (Fig. 39), the area occupied by the larvæ is divided into three

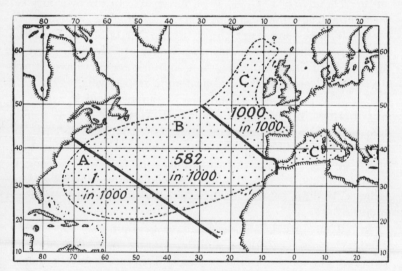

Fig. 39.   Proportions over 50 mm. long of European eel-larvae found in the Atlantic.

Illustrating the general trend, with growth, towards the coasts of Europe and Mediterranean Africa (*after Schmidt*).

parts : a western part (A) where one in a thousand only of the leptocephali exceed 50 mm.; a central part (B) where the proportion of leptocephali over 50 mm. rises to 582 per thousand; and an eastern part (C) where all the larvæ exceed 50 mm. Whatever be the method used, therefore, it becomes abundantly clear that " the main displacement of the eel larvæ is, starting from the spawning area, towards the north-east and consequently towards Europe ". (Schmidt.)

EEL POPULATIONS IN THE MEDITERRANEAN

A part of the Group II leptocephali arrives, every year, at the entrance to the Straits of Gibraltar, and enters the Mediterranean on the surface currents. It is necessary to point out that these *Atlantic larvæ are the only source for populating the Mediterranean region with eels*:

(1) The Mediterranean cruises of the *Thor* (1909–1910) and of the *Dana* (1921–1922) were never able to discover any eel leptocephali less than 50 mm. long.

(2) The eel larvæ get larger the further one goes from the Straits of Gibraltar towards the Straits of Messina. Several thousands of individuals at these extreme regions have shown an average length of 6.9 and 71.6 mm. respectively.

(3) The maximum abundance of leptocephali in winter is at Gibraltar, in spring and summer at Messina. This is consistent with the hypothesis of a movement from west to east. In any case, the surface currents in the Mediterranean, the average speed of which, from experiments carried out by the *Thor,* is 15 miles a day, would carry the leptocephali over the 2,000 km. from Gibraltar to the Straits of Messina in three to four months.

(4) There are no leptocephali to be found in the eastern Mediterranean (except at a little distance beyond Sicily and Cap Bon) or in its associated waters. This fact would be inconsistent with a spawning ground in the Adriatic or in the Ionian Sea as suggested by Grassi and Mazzarelli. On the other hand, all is explained if we admit, with Schmidt, that all the larvæ come from the Atlantic through the Straits of Gibraltar. Becoming fully grown in the surface waters above the 1,000 metre line which rings the western basin of the Mediterranean, they are transformed into elvers before entering the eastern

Mediterranean and ultimately the Black Sea. These regions, very remote from the spawning area, are comparable to the Channel, North Sea and Baltic, which also receive individuals already metamorphosed.

(5) Finally, the species *Anguilla anguilla* is perfectly homogeneous. Biometrical researches carried out by Schmidt have not made it possible to identify distinct races. This would not be so if these animals had not a single breeding ground where the differences imposed by the habitat are neutralised every year by cross-breeding.

LARVAL GROWTH

Concurrent with the larval migration there is a larval growth which lasts $2\frac{1}{2}$ years. If it were possible to obtain the complete picture, it would be necessary to divide it into three phases :

(1) An embryonic phase (embryo contained in the egg).

(2) A pre-larval phase (pre-larva or pre-leptocephalus still retaining a yolk-sac).

(3) A larval phase properly so-called (larva or leptocephalus).

In fact, the first phase is unknown, and we possess as yet only a very small number of pre-leptocephali (Fig. 36). Fortunately, the same is not true for that true larval phase, the development of which can be followed step by step *in extenso*, thanks to the works of Grassi (1913) and Schmidt (1906, 1913, 1916). Plate VII represents the first stages.

An eel leptocephalus can be compared to a willow or laurel leaf made absolutely transparent, like glass. The first thing that strikes one, even with the naked eye, it its transverse segmentation. From one end to the other, there are arranged, in regular succession, muscle segments or myotomes (μνός, muscles; τομος, section) each having the form of a double chevron fitting one into the other, (Fig. 40). The total number of myotomes varies from 110 to 119 with an average of 115. This is one of the best characteristics for distinguishing the leptocephali of the European eel from those of other species. The same number is characteristic, it will be recalled, of the vertebræ of the adult. In the leptocephali there are as yet no vertebræ. The

skeletal axis is only represented by a semi-rigid rod, the notochord, running from the head to the tip of the tail, and directly
above it the spinal cord. Later on, will appear the rudiments
of the vertebræ ringing the notochord like the beads of a rosary.

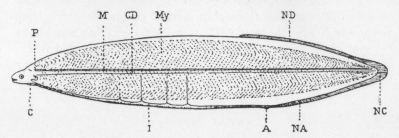

FIG. 40.   Leptocephalus of the European eel.

Earlier described under the name of *Leptocephalus brevirostris*.   *A*, anus;
C, heart; *CD*, notochord; *I*, intestine; *M*, spinal chord; *My*, myotomes;
NA, anal fin; *NC*, caudal fin; *ND*, dorsal fin; *P*, pectoral fin.

The notochord and the spinal cord divide the leptocephalus
into dorsal and ventral portions having approximately the same
size. Along the ventral edge runs the digestive apparatus in
which the intestine can be easily recognised, finishing about
two-thirds of the way along the body. The anus is below about
the 70th myotome. The transparency of the body also makes
it possible to distinguish the rudiments of the liver, kidneys,
genital organs, etc., as well as the heart, situated well forward
in an incurvation of the digestive tube, at the place where it
connects with the pharynx by a short œsophagus.

The name leptocephalus signifies " slender head ", which is
in fact no more than a very small projection from the anterior
end of the body. Under the microscope (Fig. 41) the eyes can
be seen, their black pupils contrasting with the absence of pigmentation in the rest of the body. The mouth gapes widely and
is armed with a certain number of teeth. There are, in addition,
the short muzzle to which allusion is made in the expression
brevirostris used by Kaup to qualify the leptocephalus; the
nostrils which at first are simple orifices on each side of the
muzzle, ultimately becoming doubled as they are in the greater
part of adult fishes; finally, the larval brain of which some
parts are visible above the eyes.

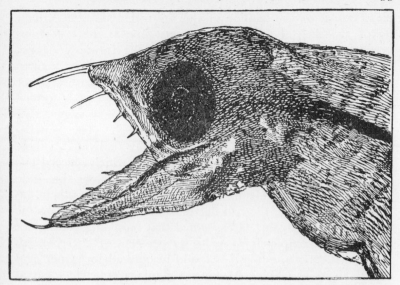

Fig. 41.   Head of a 10 mm. leptocephalus (*after Schmidt*).

The leaf-shaped body of the leptocephalus is bordered over
part of its circumference by an unpaired fin to which is given,
according to the place where it is found, the name of dorsal,
caudal and anal. This embryonic transparent fin, unprovided
with rays, begins on the head and finishes at the anus. A thin
black edge which grows slowly in length forward and breaks
up into interspinous elements, appears dorsally and ventrally,
in the most posterior part, when the leptocephalus is about
20 mm. These are not yet true rays, but the bases on which
the rays will begin to form as soon as the leptocephalus reaches
a length of about 30 mm. At 40 mm. all the interspinous
elements will have formed, and by the time the larva is 60 mm.
long all the rays will have appeared and the fins will have their
definitive appearance.

There are, therefore, two waves of differentiation which
succeed one another from the tail to the head : first that of the
interspinous elements secondly that of the rays. We shall see
later that the pigmentation of the elvers proceeds also in a
caudo-cranial direction.

The development of the caudal region is a little more complex because of the relation of this fin to the posterior extremity of the skeletal axis. At the same time as the notochord becomes covered with successive rings, the future vertebræ, there appear against its turned-up end three processes destined to serve as bases for the future rays (Fig. 42). Of these three hypurals (ὕπο, under; οὑρά, tail), the last but one is formed first and divides longitudinally. The last makes its appearance afterwards and also divides longitudinally. The antepenultimate piece is formed latest and remains undivided. There are, therefore, at a certain stage, five pieces which succeed one another from the front to the back. Now, while this state persists in a certain number of individuals, in others, as Schmidt has shown, the two halves of the last hypural become welded together again. Grassi noted that rewelding takes place more or less completely in 42 to 47 per cent of the elvers at Pisa and Leghorn, while it is found in only 28 to 34 per cent of the elvers at Naples, Messina, Catania, Comacchio and at various points on the Atlantic coast.

In the very young leptocephali, the dentition consists of only one to three teeth in each half-jaw, and this is the same in all individuals. Afterwards the number of teeth increases by successive growths. There are four per half-jaw at the size of 10 mm. (Fig. 41), nine at 30 mm., twelve at 40 mm. and so on. The maximum observed is twenty teeth in each half of the upper jaw, against nineteen for each half of the lower jaw, a total of seventy-eight teeth. The dental formula is thus written Upper: $(1 + 1 + 18)$; Lower: $(0 + 1 + 18)$. The first tooth of the upper jaw is rudimentary and slow to appear. Behind it is a long hook-shaped tooth to which Schmidt gave the name of grasping tooth. Afterwards come the back-teeth —molars in position if not in form—which line the jaw.

LARVAL PHYSIOLOGY

The food is known only from the examination of the contents of the intestine and consists solely of microplankton caught by the larval teeth. Feeding ceases when the larva is fully grown.

The respiration has been studied by Spärck (1930) on lepto-

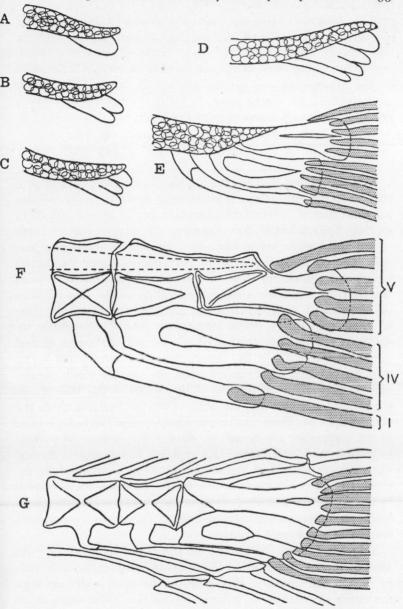

FIG. 42. Development of skeleton of tail fin in the eel.

A—D, hypural bones in the leptocephalus; *E,* splitting of the two terminal hypurals and development of rays in the growing leptocephalus; *F,* formation of vertebral centra in the elver; *G,* fusion of the two terminal vertebrae in the young eel (*after B. Grassi and J. Schmidt*).

cephali preserved alive on board the *Dana*. A micro-method allowed an estimation of the oxygen consumption of each of them for the following conditions: volume of sea water 120 to 150 cubic millimetres, temperature 18°C to 20.5°C, duration of the experiment one to one and a half hours. The results are expressed, for convenience, in cubic centimetres of oxygen per kilogramme of leptocephalus per hour:

Larva 1 year old ... ... 40 cc.
„ 2 „ „ ... ... 115 cc.
„ 2½ „ „ ... ... 420 cc.

This shows first that respiration increases in intensity in proportion to the animal's age; and second that, it always remains less than that of a leptocephalus belonging to one of the other species. Spärck has in fact compared the oxygen requirements of eel and conger larvæ taken at Gibraltar at about one year old. The consumption is 40 cc. per kilogram-hour for the eel larvæ, and 180 cc. for those of the conger. He concludes from this that the markedly reduced respiration in the first explains the slowness of their development and the exceptional duration of their growth. A feeble respiratory intensity generally indicates a reduced muscular activity. In fact, the larvæ studied remained immobile in the experimental container. But is this state an habitual one? In the open sea, are the larvæ passive and do they allow themselves to be carried at the will of the waves and currents of the sea? This is doubtful from the observations of Dean (1912) on some conger larvæ kept alive in an aquarium for about 15 days. The author saw them swimming and undulating with rapidity in the water; he saw them retract and twist themselves up when stimulated by the touch from a pencil-point on the snout. In short, they behaved in a very active manner. It is unlikely that eel leptocephali, having a similar musculature to that of the conger leptocephali, behave in a different manner.

Schmidt (1906) found that eel larvæ put in a bucket with sand or mud at the bottom did not show any tendency to hide in it. On the contrary, they swim in the open water amongst the entire population of pelagic organisms. These same leptocephali gave proof of a very strong phototaxis since they went down deep during the day and came to the surface at night (nycthemeral cycle).

BIBLIOGRAPHY

DEAN, B.   Changes in the behaviour of the eel during transformation. *Ann. New York Ac. Sc.*, XXII, (New York, 1912).

GRASSI, B.   Metamorfosi dei Murenoidi: Ricerche sistematiche ed ecologiche. (Jena, 1913).

LE DANOIS, E.   *L'Atlantique: Histoire et vie d'un océan.* (Paris, 1938).

SCHMIDT, J.   Contributions to the life history of the eel. *R. Pr. Verb. Cons. Int. Expl. Mer.*, V, (Copenhagen, 1906).

Remarks on the metamorphosis and distribution of the larvae of the eel. *Medd. Komm. Hav und. Fiskeri*, III, (Copenhagen, 1909).

Danish researches in the Atlantic and Mediterranean on the life history of the freshwater eel. *Int. Rev. Hydrob. Hydrogr.*, V, (Leipzig, 1912).

On the identification of Muraenoid larvae in their early stages. *Medd. Komm. Hav und. Fiskeri,* IV, (Copenhagen, 1913).

On the early larval stage of the freshwater eels and some other North Atlantic Muraenoids. *Idem*, V, (1916).

The breeding places of the eel. *Smithsonian Report*, 25, (Washington, 1924). This summarises the Author's work down to the discovery of the location.

L'immigration des larves d'anguilles, dans la Méditerranée, par le détroit de Gibraltar. *C.R. Ac. Sc.*, CLXXIX, (Paris, 1924); and *La Nature*, (Paris, 1924).

SCHOTT, G.   Oceanographie und maritime Meteorologie. *Wiss. Erg. Deutsch. Tiefsee Exp. Valdivia,* (Jena, 1902).

SPÄRCK, R.   Über den Sauerstoffverbrauch bei Aallarven und einigen anderen pelagischen Tieren. *Arch. Zool. Ital., Congr. Int. Zool.*, (Padua, 1930).

CHAPTER VIII

Metamorphosis and Invasion of Continental Waters

THE larval migration towards Europe finally reaches the surface, over the great depths which immediately precede the continental shelf. Having attained their full term of growth, the larvæ then undergo a metamorphosis into young transparent eels, or elvers, and it is these which, endowed with an increased activity, cross the coastal zones and make their ascent into freshwater. The larval migration and the ascent lead to a habitat, the precise limits of which we must examine.

METAMORPHOSIS

Discovered in 1896 by Grassi and Calandruccio, the metamorphosis was especially studied by Schmidt (1906–1909) and later by Grassi (1913) in his large work on the metamorphosis of the Apodes. These workers were led to divide the metamorphosis into a certain number of phases or stages which are indicated in the following table and represented in part in Fig. 43. Admittedly, such a division is necessarily arbitary in a continuous phenomenon. Such as they are, however, these stages are very useful as guides for assessing and comparing the respective ages of various individuals.

The metamorphosis involves morphological and physiological phenomena. Among the first, one of the most apparent is the change in the proportions of the body. The leptocephalus is leaf-like, very broad in relation to its length, and very thin in relation to its breadth. These two characters are modified by a process which begins at the extremities of the body and

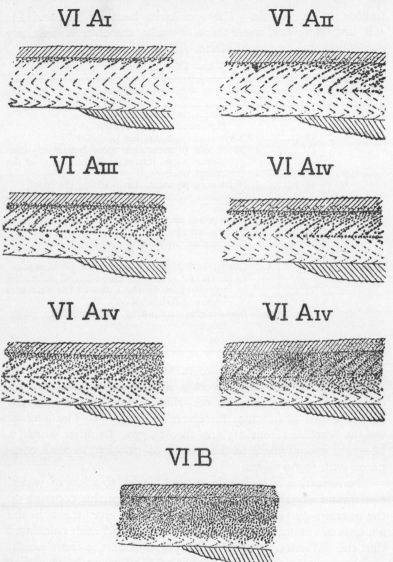

FIG. 43. Progressive pigmentation in the anal region of the elver in stages VIA and VIB.

The pigmentation extends from the upper side downward, and from the back towards the front (i.e. right to left in the figure).

finishes in its middle. The semi-larva becomes less and less tall, and more and more thick. Finally, the elver is definitely sub-cylindrical or anguilliform (Plate 8).

TABLE IX

Designation	Stages		Pigmentation
Larva	I		Leptocephalus at full growth. Pigmentation only ocular.
Semi-larva .	II		Nerve-cord pigmentation posterior.
	III		Nerve-cord pigmentation more extensive. Cutaneous pigmentation at the extremity of the caudal fin.
	IV		Nerve-cord pigmentation reaching the head. Cutaneous pigmentation invading all the caudal fin.
Elver	V	A...	No cerebral nerve-cord spot. Caudal cutaneous pigmentation.
		B...	One cerebral nerve-cord spot (Fig. 44).
	VI	A...	Caudal and maxillary cutaneous pigmentation. I, II, III, IV (Fig. 43). Dorso-lateral cutaneous pigmentation to the limits of the muscular segments (zebra aspect).
		B...	Dorso-lateral cutaneous pigmentation, generalised.
Anguillettes or " nearly yellow eels ".			

Associated with the change in form is a reduction in the length and weight. The average length of hundreds of individuals from the same source, ranges from 75 mm. for the leptocephalus to 60 mm. for elvers of stage VI. The average weight decreases from 1·5 gm. to 0·15 gm. In other words, a kilogram is equivalent to the weight of 700 leptocephali compared with 7,000 elvers.

The reduction in weight is principally due to a loss of water. Callamand (1943) calculated that a leptocephalus contains on the average 93 per cent of water, while an elver taken in the sea does not contain more than 80 per cent. Schmidt calculated that the reduction is equal to 90 per cent of the fresh weight and 30 per cent of the dry weight of the leptocephalus. With the dehydration of the tissues, in consequence, there is an intense consumption of reserves. The metamorphosis is here, as elsewhere, a crisis in growth and shows itself as a pathological phenomenon.

When they are entirely transparent, many elvers still have a slightly flattened form recalling the willow leaf form of the leptocephalus. Later on they become perfectly cylindrical and emaciation reduces them to mere filaments. Some are hardly more than skin and skeleton. The head, being undiminished in volume appears to be enormous. From the culinary point of view, the transparent elvers are fleshy, white when cooked and much esteemed (as in the elver cheese of the Severn, the elver omelette of the Landes and of Spain, and in pâtés). Once pigmented, they are tough, without flesh and on cooking become dark. They are then, on the other hand, more resistant to asphyxia and can better survive transportation for restocking.

At stage VIA the elvers begin to feed, and cease in consequence to get thinner. Their growth curve (Fig. 38) rises very quickly at first and continues its ascent more slowly, during the whole growing life as the yellow eel.

As we have seen, the leptocephalus possesses a dentition composed of several long and very fragile teeth. These larval teeth disappear in the course of the metamorphosis and are replaced in the elvers by the definitive teeth of the eel.

A curious phenomenon is the displacement of the anus towards the head, by a shortening of the intestine, as the metamorphosis is completed. The pre-anal distance falls from 70 per cent to 40 per cent of the total length of the body, which means that the anus, first situated in the posterior half, advances progressively into the anterior half where its position becomes stabilised. This might be a relative displacement, due to an unequal growth of the trunk and the tail. The proof that it is nothing of the sort is that the position of the anus varies to the same degree and in the same way if, instead of measuring it in millimetres, one marks it by the myotomes or muscle segments running from one end of the body to the other. There are initially 70 pre-anal myotomes, and finally 35, out of about 115 of which the bodies of the semi-larvæ and elvers are composed. The present author (1926) studied the anal migration in different species of Apodes. He expressed the extent of this migration by the difference, expressed in percentages of the total number of the myotomes, between the number of pre-anal segments before and after the metamorphosis. For example, in the eel we have:

$$(70 - 35)/115 \times 100 = 30$$

The values obtained for the various genera were: *Sphagebranchus* 0, *Murœna* 5, *Anguilla* 30, *Conger* 45, *Synaphobranchus* 50, *Nemichthys* 65. The eel occupies, therefore, an average position from the point of view of its metamorphosis. It is not in the extent of this last that its interest from a biological point of view lies. The table on page 140 shows that the extension of the pigment is particularly useful in classifying the successive stages of the metamorphosis. Gilson (1908) and Strubberg (1913) laid down the basis of the classification in use today: division of the semi-larvæ into stages II, III and IV; division of the elvers into stages VA, VB, VIA and VIB, themselves subdivided into secondary stages (Fig. 43).

A deep nerve-cord or meningeal pigmentation begins to form first and a superficial or cutaneous pigmentation makes its appearance a little later. Both of these develop from the tail towards the head, that is to say in the same way as the displacement of the anus, and in the same way also as the formation of the unpaired fins in the leptocephalus. Whether it be meningeal or cutaneous the pigmentation consists of a constantly increasing deposit of melanin in the interior of the stellate cells known as melanocytes and melanophores. One of the most curious formations is the cerebral pigment spot which appears at stage VB on the membranes enclosing the larval brain. It takes the form of a crown and is properly visible only through a large fontanelle (Fig. 44). Later on, it disappears beneath the superficial pigment and under the dermal bones which close the fontanelle. It can be found by trepanning, in the adult eel, in the meninges of the mid-brain (optic-lobes). Gilson insists strongly and with good reason on the importance of this spot to which he attributes a protector role against exposure to the sun. " Its precocious appearance ", he said, " about the time that the animal ceases to be pelagic, and in the immediate neighbourhood of the brain, in the open region of the cranium, is not a phenomenon of secondary importance . . . . It seems natural to interpret it by supposing that the middle region of the brain needs to be protected against the light, in

line with the big discontinuity in the cranium or primitive
fontanelle ".

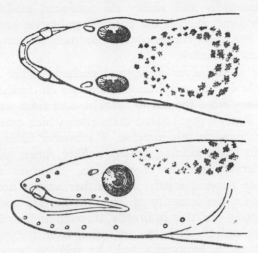

FIG. 44. Cerebral pigmentation
in the elver at stage VB (*after
G. Gilson*).

But it must be remarked that at the moment when the stain
appears, the whole cranium is translucent and unpigmented.
The light comes, therefore, to the brain from all the sides at
once. Why should it be that its upper surface should alone be
protected by a pigmentary screen? Why, on the other hand,
is the cerebral spot annular? Why, finally, does it not appear
in the fry of other fishes? Would their brains be less sensitive
to solar radiation than those of the elvers? There are so many
problems that will most probably not be resolved except by
experiment. Is Strubberg's scale capable of being applied to
all the phenomena of metamorphosis, and not only to the
invading of the body by the deep and superficial double pigmentation? Vilter (1944) doubted it, in the course of his
observations on the elvers from littoral pools and estuaries. He
found, in fact, in those under the probable influence of salinity,
an arresting of the pigmentation without corresponding inhibi-
tion of the processes of development and notably of the
dentition.

DETERMINISM OF THE METAMORPHOSIS

In all metamorphosis, the morphological phenomena merely express outwardly and visibly the profound modifications in the metabolism. Such is the case in semi-larvæ and elvers, in which at least two functions vary in their intensity—the respiratory and secretory.

Starting at the elver stage, and perhaps earlier still in the metamorphosis, the respiration increases in function as the animal passes from the sea to brackish and fresh waters. Fontaine and Raffy (1932) asked themselves which external factor contributes most to this increase. Freshwater differs from seawater in its lower salinity, greater acidity (lower pH), and by its considerably greater oxygenation. Now it is easy to demonstrate experimentally that neither acidity nor oxygenation influence the intensity of respiration. The lower salinity alone affects it, and that indirectly, through an increased hydration of the tissues. It is the transition from a hypertonic environment to a hypotonic one, in relation to its internal environment, which causes an increase in oxygen requirements in the elver. The striking results obtained by injections of thyroid extract in tadpoles or amblystoma larvæ (axolotls) have become quite classical. The thyroid hormone activates or completes their metamorphosis. A study of the thyroid in the young eel in course of its transformation was indicated, and Sklower, after his researches on the internal secretions in the life-history of the frog, approached this problem (1928 and 1930). He found, first, that the thyroid gland of the leptocephalus at stage I (end of growth) is extremely small and quiescent. In the semi-larvæ II, III and IV, it enlarges and becomes about ten times the size; its lobes increase in number and fill up with secretion. At last, in the elver stage V, and more still in stage VI, the thyroid enters on a new phase of rest as shown by its empty and pleated lobes. The development of the gland, therefore, parallels the metamorphosis. The same is true of the plaice; but in fishes having no metamorphosis (trout, carp), nothing like this happens.

In short, the determining factor in the metamorphosis of the eel appears to be a thyroid hormone. This fact must be compared with the action of the hypophysial, thyroidian, and genital hormones on the transformation of the yellow eel into the silver eel. The two metamorphoses that the eel undergoes are dependent upon internal secretions. The external factors can only retard or accelerate the phenomenon. This is what Strubberg (1913) showed, concerning the pigmentation. Two thousand elvers brought into the Carlsberg laboratory in Copenhagen on April 4th, 1912, were divided in four groups. The first, the control group, was preserved in formalin. The second was placed in an aquarium of salt water at 17 per thousand and at a temperature of 8 to 10°C. The third was put in equally salt water at 17 per thousand but at a temperature of 16 to 20°C. The fourth was kept in an aquarium of fresh water at 16 to 20°C. In other words, three groups were placed in cold sea water, tepid sea water, and tepid fresh water respectively. The elvers remained for 12 days, at the end of which their pigmentation, their loss in length and their wasting could be assessed by comparison with the control group (Fig. 45).

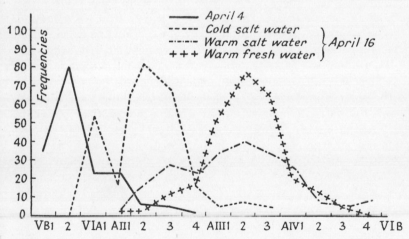

FIG. 45. Influence of temperature on pigmentation in elvers.

Number of specimens plotted vertically, state of pigmentation (cf. Fig 43) horizontally. The latter is more advanced in those kept in luke-warm water than in those kept in cold, and much more than in those killed on 4th April and preserved as controls (*after A. Strubberg*).

(1) In cold water, the elvers were merely a little transformed. In tepid water on the contrary, their average length, and especi-

ally their pigmentation, had undergone appreciable changes. Undoubtedly metamorphosis is a function of temperature.

(2) As to the salinity, the extremely small differences in size and weight found between the tepid fresh water elvers and the tepid salt water elvers were due solely to a greater dehydration by osmosis in the presence of salt. The equal development of the pigmentation in the two groups allows us to conclude that the metamorphosis is independent of salinity.

In fact, this last result was invalidated by Panu (1929). This author kept elvers from Arcachon for forty days, some in salt water at 25 per thousand, others in brackish water at 7 per thousand and others in nearly fresh water. The temperature was maintained at 16 to 18°C in all cases. Now, if at the end of the experiment we estimate the number of individuals that have passed from stage VIAi to stage VIAiv, we find it is respectively 40 per cent, 50 per cent and 70 per cent in proportion as one goes from maximum to minimum salinity. Salt then, has an unfavourable action on pigmentation.

Panu also found an unfavourable action from oxygenation. The pigmentation, according to his experiments, is slower in water saturated with oxygen than in water that is not renewed. Therefore, the introduction of the elvers into fresh water— water less salt, more oxygenated, and generally warmer than the sea water—has the total result of hastening in them the extension of the melanins which are the first of their pigments.

According to Vilter (1942–43–45), the action of the external environment is exercised through the hypophysis. This author succeeded, in fact, in removing the cranial gland from some transparent elvers and found that they did not pigment, though raised in fresh water and against a black background.

When the normal elvers begin to feed (stage VIAii or iii), the carotenoids, yellow-orange pigments soluble in fat, make their appearance in their turn and tend to be localised on the ventral surface. Finally, the guanins (waste substances) appear in the 'near eel' or late elvers.

MIGRATION TOWARDS THE COAST

Europe is surrounded by a shelf which sinks progressively under the waves to 200 or 300 m. and of which the width

varies from point to point, reaching 200 km. in the Bay of
Biscay, 80 km. in the Gulf of Lyons, and no more than a few
kilometres along the coasts of Spain, Provence, Italy, and elsewhere. All the seas of moderate depth such as the Irish Sea,
the Channel, the North Sea and the Baltic form part of this
continental shelf and constitute with it the immense area ex-
ploited by deep sea trawlers. Beyond it begin the great depths :
on the bathymetric charts, the isobath lines of 1,000 and
2,000 m., are generally not far from those of 200 m. These
details are essential to an understanding of the first phase of
the ascent of the young eels and their invasion of the continental waters.

Schmidt has shown very clearly that the metamorphosis
always begins over the great depths which precede the continental plateau : let us say between the isobaths of 2,000 and
200 m. It is only there that one finds, swimming in the surface
waters, in August–November, the semi-larvæ of stage II.
Those of stage III and IV are already nearer the coasts and
show, when observed in an aquarium, a greater agility than the
leptocephali. They swim more rapidly and even make leaps
out of the water. Finally, the elvers of stage V, called transparent elvers or glass eels because they have as yet no cutaneous
pigment, save at the caudal extremity, constitute the true invading form of the coastal waters. It is chiefly they which cross
the continental shelf and penetrate either the estuaries, or the
littoral lagoons. During their journey they swim higher at night
and remain at the bottom as long as there is light to restrain
their movements.

A prime fact which deserves attention is that their arrival
on the coast becomes somewhat more tardy as the continental
shelf widens. In October (Fig. 46) the elvers arrive on the
coasts of Portugal and Northern Spain. In November–
December they reach the Basque coast, and, because of its
proximity to the 1,000 m. isobath, Valentia Island in the south-
west of Ireland. January sees them appearing at Pouillac,
Rochefort, Saint Nazaire and, simultaneously, on the entire
west coast of Ireland. In February they penetrate into the
Irish Sea and the English Channel. The North Sea receives
in March the balance of the elvers which have not been ab-

sorbed by the Atlantic and Channel coasts. Others reach it by the north of Scotland, thanks to a strong current flowing, in this region, from west to east. At last, in April and May, the elvers penetrate into the Baltic.

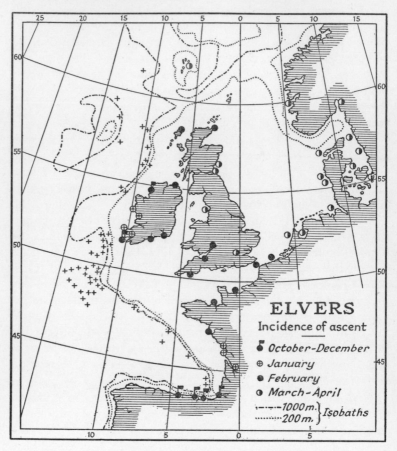

Fig. 46. Arrival of transparent elvers at the coasts.

The delay in ascent corresponds with the width of the continental shelf. Crosses show captures of leptocephali in process of metamorphosis (*after Schmidt*).

In general, the arrival of the majority of elvers is completed between October and March. This period is approximately that of the spawning in the Sargasso Sea and of the assembling

of the larvæ above the 1,000 m. isobath. These three phenomena, strictly interdependent, are only separated in time and in
space because of the journey across the Ocean. *On the
average, an eel born, for instance, in March* 1953, *reaches the
coast in March* 1956, *that is to say, when it is three years old.*

The entry into the Baltic is so late that all the elvers are pigmented (stage VI) or even transformed into little eels. Trybom and Schneider (1908) showed that they remain several
years in the seaweed-beds off the coast before entering the
freshwaters. From their observations, as well as from those of
Nordquist (1907) and Järvi (1909), the remarkable fact
emerges that the ascent in Sweden and Finland is undertaken
solely by individuals 20 to 50 cm. in length and 5 to 12 years
of age. The Baltic is like an immense estuary where the greater
part of their growth takes place.

In the Mediterranean, the problem is posed in another way.
Owing to the narrowness of the continental shelf, the penetration by the larvæ is from the Straits of Gibraltar to the Straits
of Messina and a little beyond. It is only in the eastern Mediterranean and despite the great depths that there is established a
condition approaching that of the Baltic. Only elvers at stage
V or stage VI are found there, the ascent of which is, as we
can see, somewhat more tardy in countries farther east.

If we consider now, according to the date at which it takes
place, the economic importance of the ascent at the various
points on the European coasts, a law comparable with that
above can be formulated. As was to be expected it is *the
places directly exposed to the Atlantic which receive the greatest numbers*, such as the coasts west and north of the Iberian
peninsula, the west coasts of France, Ireland and England.
Only in these regions extensive fisheries for food or re-stocking
take place. *As we move farther from the Atlantic, the arrivals
are, proportionately, less and less abundant.* Living on rivers
entering the North and Baltic Seas, the Germans were obliged
to import annually several million elvers from the Severn for
the re-population of their fresh waters. The Dutch bought in
France (from the Basse Loire) for the stocking of the Rhine.
Athanassopoulos published numerous observations (1928–
1954) on the restricted ascent of the elvers in the eastern Medi-

terranean. He contrasted the poorness of these arrivals of young eels in the Balkan Peninsula and Greek Archipelago with the wealth of arrivals in France, Spain and Italy. Only one Greek river, Alpheios, enjoys an ascent worthy of the name. It is evidently the same for Egypt, Syria and Turkey. At the entrance to the Black Sea, according to Hovasse (1927), the ascent is imperceptible.

Already so diverse in date and quantitative importance, the arrivals present yet another most curious phenomenon, brought to light by Chiappi (1934). He pointed out that if we compare the produce of the elver fisheries at the same point over several consecutive years—the chosen point was Maccarese, near Rome—we find a double periodicity very well shown in

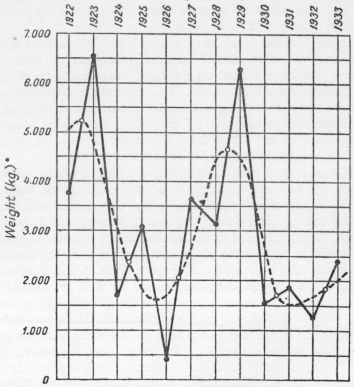

FIG. 47. Periodicity in the elver run shown by catches at Maccarese, near Rome (*after T. Chiappi.*)

the graph (Fig. 47). First, there are some annual fluctuations : every even year is marked by low captures; every odd year by high ones. Then, there is superimposed on the biennial cycle a six-yearly cycle : three years of increase followed by three years of decrease. Chiappi sees a relation between this double periodicity and the areas of heavy rainfall on the Italian littoral. But does it not restrict the scope of a phenomenon, of which we can see manifestations elsewhere than in Italy, too much? Chiappi himself found that a periodicity of the same order can be observed at Bremen and at San Sebastian. From the fishing station of Nantes, M. Le Clerc, Inspector of Waters and Forests, sent me the following figures of the quantities of elvers forwarded by this re-stocking station: in 1929, 780,000 individuals; in 1930, 1,255,000; in 1931, 610,000; in 1932, 1, 273,000; in 1933, 545,000; in 1934, 1,015,000. The alternation between the good and bad years is obvious. If there are discrepancies in relation to the even and odd year catches at Maccarese, this may well be because, in the one case, the count is made during successive seasons (e.g.: 1929–30, 1930–31, etc,), and in the other during successive years (e.g.: 1930, 1931, etc.).

A remark by Gandolfi Hornyold suggests a much more general interpretation of the periodic variations of the ascent. The big elvers of 1930, he said, originated from large leptocephali met with by Schmidt a few months earlier around the Bay of Biscay. Thus the problem is no longer coastal but oceanic. It is the abundance and the sizes of the leptocephali that make the abundance and the sizes of the elvers. All variations in the last are preceded by variations in the inhabitants of the open sea, and any periodicity in the ascent must have its origins in a periodicity in the great waters. Now, what periodicity appears more constant, at the present time, than the one which has been propounded by Le Danois in the oceanic drift? One can suppose that the years of greater drift favour the growth of the leptocephali which thus arrive more numerous and larger in the neighbourhood of the coasts. It would be necessary to pursue the matter in detail before coming to conclusions.

THE ASCENT

The elvers arriving at the coast do not generally remain on the shores, but penetrate, some into the littoral pools, the others in the estuaries, then up the rivers and their tributaries. It is their " anadromous migration " (ἀνά upwards; and δρομος, course) or more simply their ' ascent '.

This most impressive biological phenomenon is seen very strikingly on the Severn in England, where in a few Spring weeks enormous quantities of elvers are taken for food, in large canvas scoops about 3 ft. × 2 ft. and 2 ft. deep, on a willow framework.

In favourable conditions, the ascent of the elvers assumes the special aspect to which, in France, the name of *cordon* is given. " Sometimes in the Basse Loire ", writes Roule, " this *cordon* measures several kilometres in length, practically un-interrupted, of about one metre in width and half a metre in depth. The elvers, by millions, congregate to form it. In full daylight, they separate, stop, spread out on the bottom, and dig into the mud or burrow among the stones. At nightfall, once more active, they resume their course and re-form the *cordon* in which each, straining to advance, profits by the efforts of its neighbours and of the whole community ".

Crespon gave, in 1844, an extremely picturesque description of the same phenomenon: " The bouyeirouns or young eels come together at the mouth of the Rhône, or rather they come out of the sea, packing in such great quantities that I have myself seen a spherical mass of them as large as a sizeable barrel. This mass rises and falls again continually in the water and gradually the individuals detach themselves to form a cord, like a ball of wool unwinding. These thousands of little eels direct themselves immediately to either side of the river and ascend it, without ever leaving its edges, in order to penetrate every little side-stream. It is in this manner that they repopu-late the freshwaters. This kind of procession lasts more than 15 days without a stop ".

All who have observed the ascending migration of the elvers remark on their vigour and perseverance, which no lock-gates, sluices, barriers or waterfalls can discourage. One sees them climb the vertical side and even leave the water provided that there is a little moisture. " At Palma in Majorca ", writes Gandolfi Hornyold, "there was a little waterfall which communicated with the ditches of the town, and it was only necessary to sweep the walls while another person caught the many little elvers in a sack ". Gilson recounts how a dyke appeared at a distance shining in the sun with a lively brilliance : " It was completely covered with young eels climbing up the bank with the help of the viscosity of their skin ". Lastly, there is a citation from Ireland, taken from *Salmonia; or Days of Fly Fishing* (1831) by none other than the celebrated English physicist Sir Humphrey Davy : " When I was at Ballyshannon, about the end of July, the mouth of the river, which had been in flood all this month, under the fall, was blackened by millions of little eels, about as long as the finger, which were constantly urging their way up the moist rocks by the side of the fall. Thousands died, but their bodies remaining moist, served as the ladder for others to make their way; and I saw some ascending even perpendicular stones, making their road through wet moss, or adhering to some eels, that had died in the attempt. Such is the energy of these little animals, that they continue to find their way, in immense numbers, to Loch Erne ".

Such reports help us to understand how the eels penetrate the smallest rivulets and find their way into fish ponds which have no outlet. It would be interesting to study how far their ascent is obstructed by the great dams associated with hydraulic power projects. We know that the Rhine waterfall at Schaffhausen does not prevent them from getting to Lake Constance. That of the Rhône (now disappeared following the construction of the dam at Génissiat), on the contrary, always stopped their ascent towards the Lake of Geneva.

MIGRATORY TAXES

When we study the details of the ascent, we see that they depend closely on a multitude of factors, such as strength and direction of the tides, prevailing winds, lunar cycle, alternation of day and night, temperature, and so on. Observers on the coast can often predict with great accuracy the extent of the

L

elver catch. All the same, Le Clerc (1930) and Arné (1931)
do not disguise the complexity of the problem. We can only
begin by breaking down what was formerly called 'migratory
instinct' into a series of elementary reactions or taxes.

(1) *Phototaxis or reaction to light.* In the sea the leptocephali and the elvers approach the surface during the night and
go down during the day. Deelder (1952) proved this anew in
the course of his enquiries on the marine migrations of elvers.
In their ascent of the rivers, the elvers travel by night and
bury themselves during the day—they are photophobic. Grassi
(1913) records some observations made at Messina by Calandruccio. An aquarium having been half covered with black
paper, the leptocephali put in it took refuge in the darkened
part. None of them passed into the lighted zone for three days.
The same results were obtained by Fontaine and Raffy (1932)
with elvers. Nevertheless, the fishermen operate with lamps. In
the lower Loire, when the ascent is well under way, you would
think, said Le Clerc, that you were at a Venetian fête. But
Heldt and Mme. Heldt (1930) observed, in the Lake of Tunis,
that the elvers are neither attracted nor repelled by light. How
can we reconcile these apparently contradictory facts? It is
possible that the phototaxis changes direction with the varying
intensity of the light, or that it can be dominated by another
taxis. Moreover, we should have to be certain that the observations are always made on elvers at the same stage of pigmentation. Melanins in the skin and meninges can serve as a screen
to the nervous centres and, at a given moment invert the taxis.

(2) *Rheotaxis or reaction to currents.* The elvers penetrate
the estuaries at the ebb-tide, proceed thereafter up the rivers
against the current; while struggling against the out-going currents they also find their way into the littoral lagoons. Weirs
and waterfalls exercise a particular attraction for them. In contrast to the stages which precede and follow them, we can say
that the elvers have altogether an inverted rheotaxis. Compared with the leptocephali, brought by the ocean-currents, or
the breeding individuals, carried away by the same currents,
their migration is active and not, like these two, virtually
passive.

Sklower (1928–30), Hagen (1936) and François (1941)

Callamand and Fontaine (1943) see in this activity of the elvers a consequence of their thyroid hypersecretion. It is, in fact, found that hyperthyroidism, in general manifests combativeness and an instinct to struggle, of which a positive rheotaxis is only one manifestation in fishes.

In his treatise on hormones, Collin (1938) gave the following picture of hyperthyroidism: " The individual seems to possess an increase of energy; it ascends slopes instead of descending them, and leaps obstacles it may meet on its way. Instead of loss of energy, surrender, abandon, incapacity to act, there is impetuosity, an urge to conquer and the craving for action." Could not this description be applied word for word to the elvers who wrestle frantically to ascend the course of the rivers and to scale every obstacle?

On the other hand, the elvers have not all the same degree of thyroid activity. Those less charged with hormones— especially the males—would remain for this reason in the littoral lagoons and the estuaries. Those richer in thyroid hormones would, on the contrary, ascend the courses of the rivers, and the more they were sustained by their secretions, the farther they would go.

(3) *Hydrotaxis or reaction to freshwater.* The arrival at the coast and the penetration of the lagoons or estuaries is always made in the direction of a decreasing salinity. It is natural to suppose, therefore, that the elvers are attracted from the open sea by the freshwater brought down by the rivers. This effect is felt at some tens of miles from the coast. On a smaller scale, Walter (1910) tells how at Comacchio the people bring about the entrance of the elvers by letting freshwater into the lagoons. Near Tunis, at Sidi-Daoud, an irrigation canal empties into the sea, and the freshwater flowing out brings about a massive ascent of elvers. In the Lake of Tunis, in which the water is on the contrary more salt than the open sea, the elvers arrive in dispersed order. Heldt and Mme. Heldt compare this with the pumps at Mex, near Alexandria, which daily eject into the sea more than three million tons of freshwater and thus form a formidable attraction for elvers. The periods when the pumps were working were also those of ascent—e.g. December in 1921, November in 1922, October in 1923. The quantity

of young eels taken in this veritable freshwater trap is enormous; more than six million individuals were taken in 1920 and used for re-stocking the interior lakes of Egypt.

The attraction of freshwater for the elvers can also be demonstrated experimentally. In a tank containing salt water, Sylvest (1931) immersed a number of bottles, some filled with freshwater, others with sea water, disposed in different ways. He found that elvers placed in the bucket all entered the bottles of freshwater.

Just as they explain, by the demineralisation of the tissues, the need shown by silver eels to leave the freshwater and make for the sea, Fontaine and Callamand (1941) invoke an inverse phenomenon to explain the attraction of the elvers to the freshwater. The elvers, as we have seen, undergo a considerable emaciation and an intense dehydration in the course of their metamorphosis. The thyroid takes part in this phenomenon, the final result of which, is to create an impulse in the young eels to seek a less salty environment. "These facts", conclude the two authors, "lead us to a consistent hypothesis about the determinism of a changing environment which is imposed on the eel. We think that it is not without interest to conceive of the two migrations (that of the mature individuals and that of the young) as started by internal modifications of the same nature : by a hydromineral disequilibrium of the organism".

(4) *Stereotaxis or reaction to contact with solid bodies.* Grassi (1913) reports that some leptocephali kept alive in aquaria with sand at the bottom have no tendency to bury themselves. It is only in the course of the metamorphosis, as a fairly general rule, that the need for shelter begins to be felt. The elvers finally show it in the maximum degree.

Here are some experiments carried out by Sigalas (1929) on elvers from the basin of Arcachon. Two large tanks each containing 25 litres of water were joined by a tube half immersed. One tank contained seaweeds, that could also be replaced by rubber bands, pebbles or broken glass. To vary the experiment the water in the tube could be still or flowing, or one of the tanks could be filled with sea water and the other with freshwater. In all cases it was found that the elvers ended up by settling themselves in contact with the immersed objects.

Their movements, in whatever direction, showed no other taxis than that of contact.

Without going so far as Sigalas, who denies the rheotaxis and hydrotaxis, it is evident that the mud, pebbles and plants exercise on the elvers a not negligible effect in the course of their migration. Having penetrated, for example, into a river or pool, they stay in it because of the solid bodies against which they can rub themselves. But if the stereotaxis is a fixative, it does not seem to function as a *directive* agent. It cannot be this that brings the elvers from the sea towards the coast. It would not play, despite Sigalas' experiments, more than a subordinate role to the other taxes.

(5) *Thermotaxis*. Recently, Hiyama (1952) has given evidence of the effect of temperature on the migration of the elvers of the Japanese eel. It took place principally at the times of the year when the difference between the temperature of the sea- and freshwater was least, i.e. especially in March and April for the rivers in question.

Comparative studies of taxes in elvers, yellow eels and silver eels show that, except for the negative photo-taxis, which is constant, the others are essentially variable with age. The elver is attracted by freshwater while the silver eel is attracted by sea water. The elver ascends a stream of water while the silver eel descends it. The elver seeks shelter and already shows, despite its migratory inclinations, a tendency towards the sedentary life of the yellow eel; on the other hand, the silver eel shuns the bank and keeps in the current which carries it away.

There is nothing surprising about this. Each phase of the eel's behaviour is in fact the result of its interaction with its environment. Now, both of these are variable. The external environment is not the same in autumn, when the descent takes place, as in spring for the ascent. Temperature and salinity vary according to the seasons. The autumnal flood waters have a driving force absent at seasons of low water. In the sea, the warm waters flow and ebb alternately.

In the eel itself, the changes are not less. Its internal environment acquires new properties from the intake of food and from fatigue, and charges itself, during the period of metamorphosis and sexual maturation, with internal secretions which alter its chemical properties. Finally account must be taken of the reactions of the nervous system which perfects itself in the course of a life-time. The eel is an impulsive organism whose reflexes answer at any moment to the multiple external influences. In these reflexes, the part played by the various sense-organs deserves separate study at each phase of development.

HABITAT OF THE EUROPEAN EEL

The geographical distribution is evidently the consequence of the migration of the leptocephali from the Sargasso Sea to the European coast. Wherever this migration extends, the elvers penetrate into freshwater and invade the river basins; where it does not reach, eels are not found. There is not, in biogeography, a more striking example of the interpretation of the habitat of a species as a function of its larval biology. To the splendid work that Schmidt (1909) devoted to the distribution of freshwater eels throughout the world, he gave the sub-title " a biogeographical investigation ".

To the north, the Atlantic drift brings the larvæ to Iceland and the Faeroes. On the mainland the extreme limits of distribution appear to be latitudes 23° and 71° north. They are nearly those, with a slight displacement towards the pole, of the temperate zone in the northern hemisphere.

The farther one goes north the rarer become the eels. Practically all the remunerative fisheries are south of 63° latitude. In Norway, official statistics indicated the capture, in 1908, of 65,000 kg. of eels in the southern district against 230 kg. in the northern district. Northern Russia and northern Siberia are without eels.

At the opposite limits of the habitat, on the African coasts, eels are present in Morocco but not in Senegal. Their absence is total from the Gulf of Guinea to the Cape of Good Hope. On these 5,000 miles of coast there is no lack of rivers or lagoons where the eels could live. One cannot doubt that their absence is solely because the ocean currents laden with larvæ do not go towards the shores of the southern hemisphere.

A very peculiar problem is that of the eels of the Black Sea basin. Siebold (1863), in his excellent treatise on freshwater fishes of Central Europe, remarks that eels are present in all the tributary waters of the Baltic, North Sea, Atlantic, Mediterranean and Adriatic, but are absent from those which flow into the Black Sea. They are absent, he alleges, from the basin of the Danube, Dnieper, Dniester and Don, because the waters of these rivers have properties which are noxious to them. Without pursuing this point, which is at variance with the facts, let us come to more modern authors such as Antipa (1909), Berg (1917), Hovasse (1927) and Borcea (1928-1933). With them, opinon changes and eels reputed until then to be absent from the basin of the Black Sea, are said only to be extremely rare. They are taken in the Danube, one metre in length and two to three kilogrammes in weight. The fishermen of the Dnieper and Dniester find a few of them in their nets every year; ten eels were taken in 1907 in the Bay of Burgas (Roumania), and about a score are captured annually at Sebastopol. The fisheries of the Turkish coasts supply the markets of Trebizond and Heraclea with eels, and there are eels in the Sea of Azov and in the Sea of Marmora. Every autumn, silver eels pass the Bosphorus and the Dardanelles in the direction of the Mediterranean. All the Black Sea coasts, concludes Berg, possess eels.

What can, therefore, be the cause of their rarity? It was at first supposed that the eels of the Danube had been introduced by human agency. In fact, several introductions of elvers were carried out, in Bavaria and Württemburg, about 1890. But this explanation, valid perhaps for the very big eels which would today be over sixty years old, has no value when applied to the small ones caught from time to time. Could the eels not have passed on their own from the upper tributaries of the Rhine and Elbe to the upper tributaries of the Danube through the canals which unite them? This also has been suggested and with good reason. The eels are sufficiently migratory, at certain periods of their existence, not to be stopped even by appreciable watersheds. But this hypothesis, valuable concerning the Danube, cannot be valid for other tributaries of the Black Sea.

Once again the best explanation is that resulting from Schmidt's work. The Black Sea eels originate, via the Mediterranean, from the Atlantic, as do all others. After having cleared the Straits of Gibraltar and helped to repopulate the Spanish, French, Algerian and Italian coasts, the mass of larvæ stops at the approaches to Sicily and Tunisia. From there, after metamorphosis, they invade the eastern Mediterranean and ultimately the Black Sea through the Dardanelles. But the immigrants, more and more decimated by a crowd of enemies and having lost en route, some millions of individuals to Italy, Greece, Egypt, and the Levant, are greatly reduced in number at the end of their journey. It is simply because few elvers arrive in the Black Sea that eels are so rare in all its tributary rivers.

Switzerland, watershed of all Central Europe, offers an epitome of the distribution of eels between the various water systems. All the lakes and watercourses which flow into the Aar, the Rhine and, on the southern slopes, the Ticino and Po contain an abundance of eels up to an altitude of 1,000 metres. There are some in the Lakes of Constance, Zürich, the Vierstätter, Neuchâtel, and so on. In the Lake of Geneva and in the upper Rhône eels are rare. The legend goes that St. William, Bishop of Lausanne, excommunicated them in the 15th century. More scientifically, let us say that they could not ascend the former gorge—still less the great modern dam—on the Rhône at Bellegarde south-west of Geneva, and must try to attain the these upper waters by crossing, despite thousands of obstacles, from the Lake of Neuchâtel. Lastly, eels are unknown in all those south-eastern parts of the Grisons whose waters drain into the Inn and hence the Danube basin.

Considered as a whole, the area of distribution of the European eel is characterised by the immense extent and variety of habitats. We find eels from sea-level to an altitude of 1,000 metres, in the cold waters of Iceland and Scandinavia as well as in the warm waters of North Africa. There are some in freshwater (ponds and rivers), in the seas (Baltic, Black Sea), and in brackish water (estuaries, littoral lagoons). They have been found around all the coasts. Robin (1818) cites the case of an eel taken in the Adour, whose stomach was full of marine worms and molluscs. Gilson (1908) cites a male captured at about 10 kilometres from the Belgian littoral whose stomach contents were composed entirely of marine crustaceans. Of course, these were not migratory eels on the way to the Sargasso Sea. The fact that food was found in their digestive tracts indicates on the contrary that they were growing individuals passing from freshwater to the sea and back again, a procedure made possible by the eel's remarkable resistance to change of salinity. Eels are on the whole extremely tough creatures. No other fishes known are capable of rivalling them in their resistance to such diverse surroundings.

LIFE CYCLE OF THE EUROPEAN EEL

Since in the next chapter, we shall be studying the other species of eels, let us strike a balance of what is and what is not known about the life-cycle of the European eels.

(1) The very young larvæ less than 10 mm. long are strictly confined to an area bounded by latitudes 22° and 30° north and longitudes 48° and 65° west. It is there and nowhere else, that the nuptial assembling of the European eels takes place. The spawning area thus defined is situated to the east of the West Indies and midway between it and Bermuda. It coincides with the centre of the Sargasso Sea.

(2) Within the limits of the spawning area, the very young leptocephali cannot be captured except from March to July. They are not taken in autumn or winter. Therefore, the spawning of the eels must begin in spring and continue until the middle of summer, a duration of about five months.

(3) Spawning and incubation must be accomplished at a depth of 400–500 metres where pressure, darkness and salinity, and an optimum temperature of 16 to 17°C combine to produce the most favourable conditions.

(4) A short while after hatching, the larvæ ascend towards the surface and can be taken thereafter at an average depth of 50 metres during the day, and 20–30 metres during the night.

(5) Carried by the surface currents, the larvæ disperse in all directions around the spawning area. Those that go north, south or west perish for various reasons. The leptocephali carried to the north-east, that is to say towards Europe, alone have a chance to reach a stage favourable for their metamorphosis.

(6) The duration of the larval migration is normally two

and a half years. As a result, the leptocephali can be divided into three year-groups which respectively attain, in June, an average length of 25, 53, and 75 millimetres.

(7) The larval growth is accomplished during the larval migration and is synchronised with it. Its two most remarkable phenomena are the development of the fins and the development of the dentition which furnish at all times, together with the size of the body, a means of telling the age of the individual.

(8) The metamorphosis of the leptocephali into young transparent eels, or elvers, is accomplished in autumn, above the great depths immediately adjacent to the continental shelf. The animal, which was leaf-shaped, becomes sub-cylindrical. Its length and weight diminish considerably because of the dehydration of its tissues. Its intestines become shorter. Its larval teeth fall out and are replaced by definitive teeth.

(9) Vigorous and agile, the elvers approach the coasts and continue over the continental shelf. The arrival at the coast is retarded according as the shelf is wide. It begins in October on the Spanish coast and in May in the Baltic Sea.

(10) In contact with brackish water, metamorphosis is completed. The body becomes successively charged with black and yellow pigment, the appearance of the last coinciding with the end of a fast of many months which started at the beginning of the metamorphosis. The size and weight again increases. The elvers become young eels.

(11) The growth of these yellow eels in brackish water (lagoons, estuaries) or in fresh water continues for 8 to 15 years in the male and 10 to 18 years or more in the female. It depends very much upon food, temperature, and living space. Great disparity of growth is practically always found between individuals of the same locality.

(12) From a sexual point of view, 90 per cent of eels pass successively through phases of neutrality, of precocious feminisation, and of juvenile hermaphroditism, before becoming definitely male or female. The sex appears to depend upon external circumstances (metagamic determination). However, 10 per cent of individuals are from the outset female, their sex being precociously determined (syngamic determination) and apparently independent of the environment.

(13) In the course of definitive sexual maturation, the animal ceases to feed and undergoes a new metamorphosis of which the most remarkable characteristics are, on the one hand, the degeneration of the digestive apparatus, and, on the other, the intense pigmentation of the body-surface, semi-black and silver. The yellow eel becomes a silver eel by acquiring the specific nuptial dress or, a more appropriate term, migration livery.

(14) The silver eels finally leave the fresh and brackish waters for the sea to reach their spawning place. This catadromous migration is the reverse of the anadromous migration or ascent of the elvers. Both are the result of a series of taxes or reactions of the organism to different environmental factors.

(15) The passage of the silver eels from fresh water to sea water shows their remarkable adaptability to changes in salinity. This euryhalinity is in part an osmotic equilibrium spontaneously established between the constituents of their internal environment.

(16) Once in the Atlantic the silver eels elude observation. It is surmised that their physical decadence does not allow them to survive a first spawning, and there is little probability, on the whole, that they continue to live in the ocean depths.

(17) Do the silver eels of the Mediterranean littoral go, like the others, to the Sargasso Sea? Or are they, on the contrary, confined to the Mediterranean and incapable of getting out? In either case, it is certain that they do not spawn in the Mediterranean. The re-populating of this sea is alone assured by leptocephali proceeding from the Atlantic across the Straits of Gibraltar.

The life-history of a European eel is composed then of three phases separated by two metamorphoses:

(*a*) Marine larval phase or phase of dispersal lasting two or three years (leptocephalus).

(*b*) First metamorphosis (leptocephalus into elver).

(*c*) Freshwater larval phase or phase of growth lasting 8 to 18 years (yellow eel).

(*d*) Second metamorphosis (yellow eel into silver eel).

(*e*) Adult marine phase or phase of reproduction, of unknown duration (silver eel).

According to this conception, the yellow eel is a second larva which, succeeding the first or leptocephalus larva, prepares the true imago to which one gives the name of silver eel.

BIBLIOGRAPHY

ATHANASSOPOULOS, G. Sur les montées restreintes des civelles dans la partie orientale de la Méditerranee. *C.R. Ac. Sc.*, Vol. CLXXXVI, (Paris, 1928).
Sur la montée d'anguille en 1936–1937. *Bull. Inst. Ocean*, 757, (Monaco, 1938).
Observations suivies sur la montée en Grèce. *Univ. Thessaloniki*, (1954).
BERTIN, L. Les migrations de l'anus au cours de la métamorphose chez les Poissons Apodes. *Bull. Soc. Zool. France*, Vol. LI, (Paris, 1926).
CALLAMAND, O. L'anguille Européenne. Les bases physiologiques de sa migration. *Ann. Inst. Océan.*, Vol. XXI, (Paris, 1943).
CHIAPPI, T. Persistenza di un ciclo nella montala delle sieche e variazoni nelle piogge estive. *Boll. Pesca Piscic. Idrob.*, Vol. X, (Rome, 1934).
DEELDER, C. L. On the Migration of the Elver at Sea. *J. Cons. Int. Expl. Mer*, 18, II, (Copenhagen, 1952).
FONTAINE, M. Quelques données récentes sur le mécanisme physiologiques des migrations de l'anguille européenne. *Bull. Franc. Pisc.*, Vol. XVII, (Orléans, 1944).
FONTAINE, M. and CALLAMAND, O. Sur certains facteurs des migrations de l'anguille. *Bull. Soc. Zool. France*, Vol. LXVI, (Paris, 1941).
Sur l'hydrotropisme des civelles. *Bull. Inst. Océan*, No. 811, (Monaco, 1941).
Les aspects physiologiques d'une " vie cyclique " de l'Anguille d' Europe. *Bull. Mus. Paris*, Ser. 2, Vol. XV, (Paris, 1943).
FONTAINE, M. and RAFFY, A. Recherches physiologiques sur les civelles. *Bull. Inst. Océan*, No. 603, (Monaco, 1932).
FRANCOIS, Y. Evolution de la thyroïde chez les civelles. *C.R. Trav. Fac. Sc.*, Vol. I, (Marseilles, 1941).
GILSON, G. L'anguille, sa reproduction, ses migrations et son intérêt économique en Belgique. *Ann. Soc. R. Zool. Malac. Belgique*, Vol. XLIII, (Brussels, 1908).
GRASSI, B. *Metamorfosi dei Muraenoidi.* Chap. VII, (Jena, 1913).
HAGEN, F. VON Die wichtigsten Endokrinen des Flussaals. *Zool. Jahrb., Anat.*, Vol. LXI, (Jena, 1936).
HELDT, H. and Mme HELDT. Sur les modalités de l'empoissonnement en anguilles du lac de Tunis. *Notes St. Océan. Salammbo*, No. 13, (Tunis, 1930).

HIYAMA, Y.   Thermotaxis of eel when ascending river mouth. *Jap. J. Ichthyology*, 2, I, (Tokio, 1952).

HOVASSE, R.   L'anguille en mer Noire et en mer de Marmara. *Bull. Soc. Zool. France*, Vol. LII, (Paris, 1927).

JÄRVI, T. H.   Beobachtungen über die Grösse und das Alter der Aalen in Binnengewässern Finlands. *Medd. Soc. Fauna Flora Fennica*, (Helsingfors, 1909).

LE CLERC, J.   L'anguille dans le bassin de la Loire. *Bull. Franc. Piscicult.*, Vol. II, (Orléans, 1930).

NORDQUIST, O.   Some observations about the eel in Finland. *Medd. Soc. Fauna Flora Fennica*, (Helsingfors, 1907).

PANU, A.   *Les pigments du tégument de l'anguille.* Thesis, (Paris, 1929).

SCHMIDT, J.   Contributions to the life history of the eel. *Rapp. Pr. Verb. Cons. perm. int. Expl. Mer*, Vol. V, (Copenhagen, 1906). Remarks on the metamorphosis and distribution of the larvæ of the eel. *Medd. Komm. Hav. Fisk.*, Vol. III, No. 3, (Copenhagen, 1909). On the distribution of the freshwater eels (Angilla) throughout the world. I. Atlantic Ocean and adjacent regions. A biogeographical investigation. *Idem*, No. 7, (1909).

SIGALAS, R.   Quelques observations sur la biologie des civelles du bassin d' Arcachon. *Actes Soc. Linn.*, Vol. LXXXI), (Bordeaux, 1929).

SKLOWER, A.   Das Verhalten der Schilddrüse in der Metamorphose des Aales. *Zeitsch. vergl. Physiol*, Vol. VII, (Berlin, 1928). Die Bedeutung der Schilddrüse für die Metamorphose des Aales und der Plattfische. *Fortschr. nat. Forsch.*, Vol. VI, (Berlin, 1930).

STRUBBERG, A.   The metamorphosis of elvers as influenced by outward conditions. *Medd. Komm. Hav. Fisk.*, Vol. IV, No. 3, (Copenhagen, 1913).

SILVEST, F.   Om Betydningen of Kemotaxis og Rheotaxis for Glasaalenes Vandring. *Naturens Verden*, (Copenhagen, 1931).

TRYBOM, F. and SCHNEIDER, G.   Das Vorkommen von "Montée" und die Grösse der kleinsten Aale in der Ostsee und in deren Flüssen. *Rapp. Pr. Verb. Cons. perm. Int. Expl. Mer.*, Vol. IX, Copenhagen, 1908).

VILTER, V.   Recherches sur la livrée pigmentaire de l'anguille. *Bull. Mus. Hist. nat.*, Vol. II, 1942; Vol. III, 1943, (Marseilles). Comportement de la thyroïde dans la métamorphose de la civelle d'anguille. *C.R. Soc. Biol.*, Vol. CXXXVIII, (Paris, 1944). Dissociation biologique et expérimentale du complexe morphogénétique de la métamorphose chez la civelle. *Idem.* Rhétropisme de la civelle et activité thyroïdienne. *Idem.*

Hypophysectomie chez la larve d'anguille (civelle) et reper-
cussions sur la métamorphose pigmentaire.   *Idem,* Vol.
CXXXIX, (1945).

Action de la thyroxine sur la métamorphose larvaire de
l'anguille.   *C.R. Soc. Biol.,* 140, (Paris, 1946).

CHAPTER IX

The World of Eels

BEFORE drawing general conclusions on the biology of the eel, it is important to extend the subject and to consider, in addition to the European eel, the other species of the temperate regions and of the equatorial regions. From this "world of eels" can be made deductions which would not otherwise appear. This generalisation in fact contains the key to the whole problem.

Five species of eel live permanently in the north and south temperate zones and spread only moderately into the inter-tropical zone. They are :

Anguilla anguilla, of Europe, Iceland and North Africa;
Anguilla rostrata, of North America and Greenland;
Anguilla japonica, of China and Japan;
Anguilla dieffenbachi and *Australis*, of Australia, the Auck-land Isles and New Zealand.

A strange thing is that none exists in the South Atlantic nor on the Pacific coast of America (Fig. 48)—a fact to be ex-plained in due course.

THE AMERICAN EEL

The American eel is distinguished from the European by the number of vertebræ: 103 to 110 instead of 110 to 119. This difference is already present in the myotome numbers of the leptocephali and enables us to distinguish the one from the other when they are met with together in the Sargasso Sea.

As shown on the map, the American eel is found from the southern point of Greenland to the Gulf of Mexico and the West Indies. Therefore, it encroaches fairly considerably on

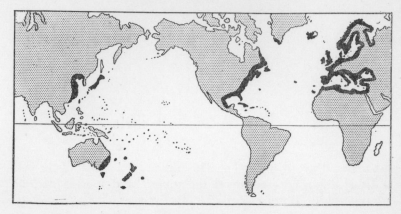

Fig. 48.   Distribution of eels in the temperate zones
(*after Schmidt*).

the sub-tropical zone. On the whole, its range is less extensive in latitude, and more to the south, than that of the European eel.

Is the absence of eels from the Pacific side of North America due to reasons of terrestrial history or to a material impossibility of existence? Smith (1896) reported that the carp and several other species from the Atlantic side—even sardines and salmon —have been easily acclimatized on the Pacific side. The attempts made with eels have always been, on the contrary, unsuccessful. All the individuals put down in 1874, 1879 and 1882 in the Californian waters were content to live and prosper without becoming established. The last were fished in 1894. What can we conclude from this, except that no spawning area acceptable by them is to be found in the North Pacific? Where is their spawning area in the Atlantic? We can surmise that it is more to the south and warmer than that of the European eel. But is it in the Gulf of Mexico or in the Atlantic? An examination of the fishing statistics shows that 98 per cent of the captured eels are from the rivers of the Atlantic coast and 2 per cent only from the rivers flowing into the Gulf of Mexico. Evidently the spawning must take place in the open sea well away from the coast of Florida, otherwise the modest coastal rivers, and the lower course of the St. Lawrence—

downstream from the Niagara Falls which the eels cannot surmount—could never compete with the vast Mississipi basin.

The Gulf of Mexico must be at a disadvantage in the same
way and for the same reason as the Black Sea or Baltic Sea
which, being too remote from the Sargasso Sea, receive only a
minimal share of elvers.

Thus the spawning area of the American eel must certainly
be in the western part of the North Atlantic, a little more to
the south and west than that of the European eel. It was there
that Schmidt discovered by chance the first leptocephali of
Anguilla rostrata and found that their mixing, at the limit of
the spawning areas, with those of *Anguilla anguilla* made it
difficult for him to distinguish between them. The American
eel has thermal needs higher than those of the European eel;
just as it spreads less to the north and more to the south during
its period of growth (yellow eel phase), it needs a higher temperature for reproduction. Its spawning area is strictly confined
to depths of 400 metres, with the temperature of 17°C. (Fig.
35).

Another biological peculiarity of the American eel is its
earlier spawning, which begins in January to February, not in
February to March as with the other species. Lastly, its larval
growth is particularly rapid. Hatched in February, its leptocephali reach 22 mm. in April, 32 mm. in June, 40 mm. in
July, and at the end of the year their maximum size is 60–65
mm. They metamorphose in winter into elvers which invade
the continental waters in the following spring. The same series
of phenomena takes three years in the European eel, so that
the American species develops in a third of the time and must
therefore complete its migration three times as quickly.

It is the duration of the larval life which sorts out the
European and the American larvæ. Those which metamorphose earlier populate America; those later, populate Europe
(though Gandolfi Hornyold reported the chance arrival of an
American eel elver on the Spanish coast in December 1930.)
The morphological differentiation of the two species was perhaps, originally, connected with this single biological difference
which has brought about a secondary increase in the number of
vertebræ in the species of slower and longer growth.

M

THE JAPANESE EEL

Just as this eel is like the European eel in its morphological characters, so also is it like the American eel in its biology. The Japanese eel extends over Japan south of Hakodate, to Formosa and, on the China coast, from Korea to Hong Kong. Chevey (1936) found it also in Tonkin.

The extensions in latitude of the three species of the southern temperate zone are :

Anguilla anguilla : 23° to 70° north.
Anguilla rostrata : 5° to 60° north.
Anguilla japonica : 20° to 42° north.

Thus the Japanese eel does not go as far north as the European eel nor as far south as the American eel. Its power of adaptation is clearly inferior to that of the two other species. Biologically it is little different from them during its period of growth, or in the course of its sexual maturation. From yellow, it becomes silvery in autumn and makes its descent towards the sea. The Cantonese call it "black ear" as do the Italian and the Tunisian fishermen.

It goes without saying that the silver eel is the object in Japan of an energetic commercial fishery equal to that in Europe and North America. Then the eel disappears in the sea. In the spring the elvers appear and ascend the fresh waters. According to official statistics the only fisheries worthy of the name are on the coast facing the Pacific. There is, on the contrary, practically none on the side of the Sea of Japan. Off the Isle of Hondo, in 1926, 3,370,000 kg. were fished on the one coast, against 150,000 kg. on the other. We may conclude that the spawning area is in the Pacific, and that the Sea of Japan and the China Seas are invaded only secondarily by the larvæ. It is a repetition of the phenomenon found many times in Europe (Baltic Sea, Black Sea), and in America (Gulf of Mexico). The populating by eels of any region is directly proportional to the distance from the spawning area. This last is exactly what is found in *Anguilla japonica*. This can only be, in relation to Japan, a situation analogous to that of the spawning ground of *Anguilla rostrata* in relation to the U.S.A. (Fig. 49).

Between 20° and 30° north there exists a water basin suffi-

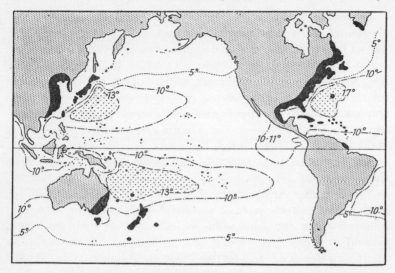

Fig. 49. Breeding areas of Japanese, Australian and American eels.

With isotherms at 400 metres depth (*after Schmidt*).

ciently warm to assure the fertilisation, spawning and incubation of the eggs; there alone persists a current, the Kuro Siwo, analogous to the Gulf Stream and capable of ensuring the dispersal of the larvæ. In addition, the thermal needs of the Japanese species are clearly less than those of the North Atlantic species. At a depth of 400 metres the isotherm which bounds its spawning area is that of 13°C and not those of 16°C and 17°C. Lastly, the larval growth of the Japanese eel lasts one year and allows it only to populate the Asiatic coasts. No species has found it possible to cross the Pacific and to colonise the American coast.

AUSTRALASIAN EELS

In Australasia there are four species of eels of which only one, *Auguilla australis*, belongs to the temperate zone and extends, on the east coast, from Sydney to Melbourne and Tasmania. Farther east, in New Zealand, it shares the habitat with a quite different species, *Anguilla dieffenbachi*, from which it is distinguished specifically by a short dorsal fin.

Australian and New Zealand eels are regularly fished by the aboriginal natives and play a great part in their mythology. The Maori language has several names to describe them: *tuna-toke* is the sedentary eel (our yellow eel) which is taken by fishing line; *tuna-heke* is the silver eel which makes its catadromous migration. To take it—seeing that it is nourished only with water and foam, says the legend—you must renounce bait and use nets. In this respect, the Maoris are inventive, since they know how to establish across the rivers, barriers with eel-traps, called *pa-tuna* which resemble surprisingly the *bordigues* and the *lavorieri* of Europe.

The fact that Australian and New Zealand eels are confined to the most easterly part of an area which could be, *a priori,* infinitely more extensive seems to indicate that their spawning ground is situated north-east of this habitat. A temperature chart at a depth of 400 metres (Fig. 49) shows exactly, at this point, an area running from west to east delimited by the isotherm of 13°C.

Just as the Gulf Stream and the Kuro Siwo scatter the larvæ

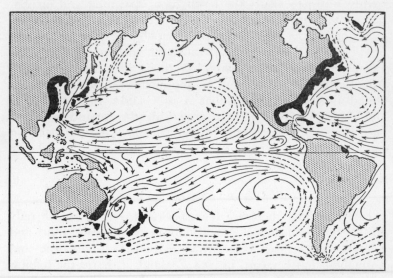

FIG. 50.   Rôle of ocean currents in disseminating larvae of the temperate eels.

of other species from south-east to north-west, the Notonectian Current of the same kind but of inverse direction ensures the transport of the leptocephali from north-east to the south-west, to the coasts of Australia and New Zealand. Round the periphery of the Tasman Sea (Fig. 50) sweeps a current which successively bathes New Caledonia, Australia, Tasmania, the Auckland Islands and the North and the South Islands of New Zealand. On so short a journey the Australian eel larvæ must have, necessarily, a rapid growth to be able to metamorphose and invade the littoral waters in time. Their biology is, therefore, comparable to that of the American and Japanese eels, and contrasts with that of the European eel. Here, again, no species has been capable of extending its larval life to cross the entire South Pacific and reach the Peruvian coasts.

GEOLOGY AND THE TEMPERATE EELS

Three major facts are revealed from the study of the temperate eels:

(1) Their spawning areas are all situated in western parts of the two great oceans.

(2) Their habitats also include the western coasts of the Atlantic and the Pacific.

(3) But the European eel stands out as going from a spawning ground in the west to populate the east coasts of the North Atlantic.

Let us try to explain these various peculiarities. We shall see later that eels swarm in the sub-tropical regions and attain their maximum differentiation there. It is, therefore, probable that the genus *Anguilla* took birth in the warm, very salt waters of the Mesogene, a kind of gigantic Mediterranean which circled the globe during the Secondary and the beginning of the Tertiary ages. It is in the deposits of this sea that one finds most of the fossil eels, from the Cretaceous (Lebanon), through the Eocene (Monte Bolca), the Oligocene (Aix-en-Provence), to the Miocene (Oeningen), and so on.

On the whole, the sub-tropical zone must have played in geological times the role of an " eel nursery ". The temperate species took birth there as did all the others before emigrating

by degrees to the various oceans. We must not confuse these
" phylogenic migrations " with the " ontongenetic migrations "
of individuals who accomplish each year their reproduction,
and of the subsequent larvæ. But the first have led to the
second. It is because the temperate eels have a sub-tropical
origin that they continue to go to the warm waters to spawn
and make long journeys to reach them. Having become, in the
adult state, able to live in the most varied climates, they have
remained faithful to the conditions of their ancestral life in the
matter of reproduction.

Now, where, in the various oceans, are the warmest and most
saline areas to be found? Precisely in their western parts, where
they are bounded, at a depth of 400 metres, by the isotherm of
13°C. in the Pacific and that of 16°C. in the North Atlantic.
Analogous conditions are not realised in the South Atlantic.
So the coasts of the Argentine, Brazil and Africa, so rich in
immense river basins where the adult eels could live perfectly,
remain totally and irremediably without them.

The dispersal of larvæ is an affair of marine currents
completed or not by oceanic drifts. Which are these currents
which ceaselessly move the mass of oceanic water? Leaving
aside, for the moment, the details of their ramifications, we can
reduce them to four great circulatory movements, of which
there are two for the Atlantic, two for the Pacific: two for the
northern hemisphere and two for the southern hemisphere
(Fig. 51). Each current receives its impetus from the trade
winds and consists initially, therefore, of a north equatorial or
south equatorial current which, moving along the equator from
east to west (contrary to the movement of the earth), is deflected
as it approaches the coasts and is turned back on itself by the
temperate regions. They circulate clockwise in the northern,
anticlockwise in the southern, hemisphere. The Gulf Stream,
the Kuro Sivo and the Notonectian current are the returning
branches of the north equatorial and south equatorial currents,
which impinge on the coasts of North America, Asia, and
Australia. If we reflect that these several currents cross the
spawning grounds previously defined, we shall see that they
bring the leptocephali to the very coasts where the adult eels
live and from whence the breeding individuals depart.

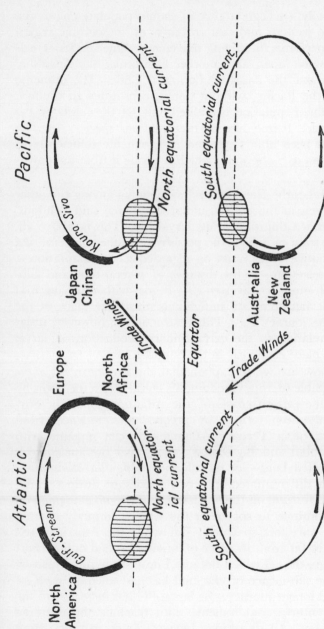

FIG. 51. Diagram of action of ocean currents.

Note that those of northern and southern hemispheres circulate in opposite directions. Shaded areas are breeding regions, black areas those where elvers reach land. The absence of eels from the South Atlantic is contrasted with the presence of two species in the North.

Theoretically, each great current should populate one or the other of the western and eastern banks of the oceanic region in which it performs its circling movement. One species of eels should populate Japan and another California, one Australia, and another one the coast of Peru and Chile. The immense breadth of the Pacific, without doubt, constitutes an obstacle and the double population is realised only for the coasts of the North Atlantic. It may also be that only one species, *Anguilla anguilla*, has been able to extend its larval life sufficiently to cross the 5,000 to 7,000 miles which separate it from its spawning area.

" What makes the European eel exceptional among the other fishes and even in the entire animal kingdom," said Schmidt, " is the extended duration of its larval life. This is, above all, a migratory state of which the persistence in the course of the three consecutive years must be regarded as an adaptation— effected by selection—to the distance of several thousand kilometres which must be traversed . . . It goes without saying that a formidable hecatomb of individuals must take place in the course of the journey . . . This destruction is, however, insignificant in relation to the extraordinary production of larvæ which takes place each year in the Sargasso Sea ".

Finally, how are we to explain that the European eel *alone* has been capable of thus extending its larval life to the point of populating the eastern coasts of the Atlantic? Since the Sargasso Sea has been formed by progressive subsidence, from west to east, of a Tertiary Atlantis, one can imagine with Germain, Joubin and Le Danois (1923) that the ancient eels of this engulfed land—let us call them *Anguilla atlantidis*— having been differentiated into two species or distinct varieties, *Anguilla rostrata* on the one hand, and *Anguilla anguilla* on the other, continue to spawn in the waters, formerly coastal, where their ancestors spawned. But while the American eel, remaining not far from its place of origin, has had only a short distance to go, the eel which became European by progressively following the subsidence of the land has had to adapt itself to a longer and longer journey. Its larval life has increased in the course of centuries and millenia until reaching the duration possessed today. All its strange biology comes, in short, from its troubles during the course of a long succession of geological events.

We can also consider Wegener's view that the Atlantic was born by separation of the continental masses formerly joined together. America moved or, as we say, drifted towards the west quicker than Eurafrica and the fissure between them has gone on widening since the beginning of the Tertiary era. Übisch (1924) takes the story up there to explain that the two species of eel have been compelled to extend their reproductive and larval migrations. But why the European more that the American? Ekman (1932) remarks with good reason that the converse would be more in agreement with the theory of Continental Drift. Since it was America that moved from Europe, it is the American eel and not the other which ought, in the course of the centuries, to have extended its migrations. Or else we should have to admit that the "primitive spawning place" has followed America in its displacement. We can see that Übisch's hypothesis fits in but imperfectly with Wegener's theory, which is itself highly debatable. A learned geologist, Termier, has said: "It is a beautiful dream, the dream of a great poet. But if one tries to embrace it, one sees in his arms only vapour and smoke. It attracts, it interests, it amuses the mind, but the solidity is missing".

INTER-TROPICAL EELS

Between the tropics extends an important zone of eels for about two-thirds of the earth's circumference. This zone comprises the Indian Ocean from Africa to the Australian coasts, and the Pacific Ocean as far as Tahiti. The eels which inhabit it are often called Indo-Pacific and are subdivided, for greater precision, into Africano-Malagasy, Indo-Malayan, Australian and Polynesian eels.

Following his voyage in 1926 to Australia, New Zealand and Tahiti, Schmidt, a little while before his death, reached some conclusions on these inter-tropical eels. The cruise round the world of the *Dana* furnished one of his collaborators, Ege (1939), with a choice of material for a vast systematic and bio-geographical study of these same animals.

First, the estimated number of species of Indo-Pacific eels must be reduced from about fifty to fourteen. Previous observers took as specific differences what have since been recognised as only individual differences. The real divisions must be founded principally on four groups of characters :

(1) The relative length of the anal and dorsal fins. As shown in (Fig. 52), pre-anal (*a*) and pre-dorsal (*d*) distances are measured and this ano-dorsal distance (*a–d*) is expressed as a percentage of the total length (*l*) of the eel. Two categories can, therefore, be established : " eels with long dorsal fins " and " eels with short dorsal fins " according to whether *a–d* is +7 to +17 per cent or only –3 to +5 per cent of the

Long dorsal-fin type

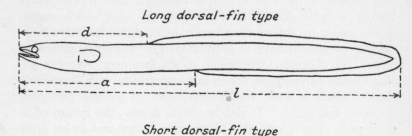

Short dorsal-fin type

FIG. 52.   Classification according to relative lengths of anal and dorsal fins.

a, pre-anal distance; *d*, pre-dorsal distance; *l*, total length.

length. (The negative values signify that the dorsal fin begins behind the anus and that *a* is smaller than *d*.)

(2) The disposition of the teeth in the palate (Fig. 53). For example the maxillary teeth may be in two or several rows; the vomerine teeth can form a median band which widens or narrows and may extend backwards as far, or not so far, as the maxillary teeth, and so on.

(3) The " dress ", which may be speckled or not, resembles in the latter case that of the European eel.

(4) The number of vertebræ—the last resource, and useful only when one has sufficient individuals to allow elimination of

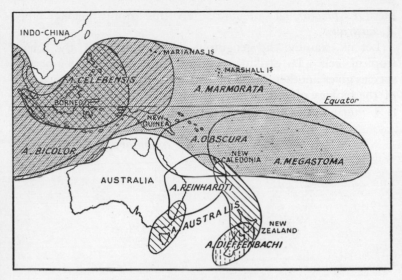

FIG. 53. Distribution of tropical eels.

Apart from *Anguilla australis* and *Anguilla dieffenbachi*, the other species may be regarded as tropical. The region to which each is ascribed includes both the seas in which it passes its marine life and the inland waters which it inhabits as a yellow eel.

the fluctuating variation and establishment of a vertebral average.

Without entering into all the details of the classification, one can say, with Ege, that the inter-tropical eels constitute four perfectly distinct groups :

First group : Species with a marbled skin and long dorsal fin, in which the maxillary teeth are in several rows close together (*Anguilla celebenis, A. megastoma*).

Second group : Species with a marbled skin and long dorsal fin, in which the maxillary teeth are in divergent rows (*A. nebulosa, A. marmorata, Anguilla reinhardti*).

Third group : Species not marbled and with long dorsal fin (*A. borneensis, A. mossambica*). Equally to this group belong most of the eels of the temperate regions and particularly those of Europe.

Fourth group : Species not marbled and with a short dorsal

fin (*A. bicolor, A. obscura*). To this group belongs also
A. australis.

Let us examine the geographical distribution of the inter-
tropical eels. Its striking contrast with that of temperate
species gives another means of extending our general knowledge
of the biology of eels. The species which has the largest habitat
is *A. marmorata* (Fig. 54). It is found, in fact, on all the Indian

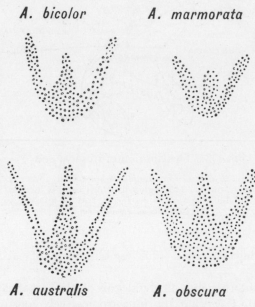

A. bicolor   A. marmorata

A. australis   A. obscura

FIG. 54. Arrangement of maxillary and
vomerine teeth in the jaws of various
species of eel (*after Schmidt*).

Ocean coasts and on most of the oceanic islands, north to the
Mariannes and south to New Guinea and New Caledonia with
the Society Islands as the eastern limit of its range. Then comes
A. bicolor which extends from the Indian Ocean to the Malayan
Islands, the Philippines and New Guinea. Two other species,
A. nebulosa and *A. mossambica,* are proper to the Indian
Ocean. *A. celebensis* inhabits Indo-Malaya, the Philippines
and western New Guinea. The habitats of *A. obscura* and
A. magastoma are to the south of the Equator, spread in long

bands, partly superposed. The first touches New Guinea, the second begins at the Solomon Isles. The maximum frequency of these species is round the isles of Eastern Polynesia : Fiji, Tonga, Samoa, Marquesas, Tuamotu, Tahiti. Finally, there remains *A. reinhardti*, whose range, rather restricted, is from New Caledonia to the eastern Australian coasts where it is superimposed on that of a temperate eel, *A. australis*.

Thus, while the whole of America and Europe have only one species of eel each, New Caledonia has five, Australia four, Tahiti three, and so on. That an island like Tahiti hardly as big as Corsica, should alone have three species of eel, is already very surprising. The surprise increases when we read the few pages that Schmidt (1927) has devoted to them. These eels, in fact, differ equally in habits and structure. *A. obscura* is an eel with a short dorsal fin and without speckles; it inhabits the stagnant and muddy waters of the littoral pools. *A. marmorata* and *A. megastoma* are on the contrary eels with a long dorsal fin and a speckled dress which harmonizes with the pebbly bottom of the inland waters; rivers of the plains for the first species, mountain torrents for the second. What a contrast between these restricted habitats and the vast area occupied, from North Cape to Morocco and from the littoral pools to the mountain lakes, by the European eel!

One feels, from this example, that the inter-tropical zone is really a zone of predilection for the eels. They attain a size never reached by temperate eels. In Europe the male rarely exceeds 45 centimetres and weighs at the most 300 grams; in Tahiti it frequently has a length of 80 cm. and a weight of 2 kg. As to the females, Schmidt cites some of 2 metres in length and 50 cm. in circumference.

The inter-tropical and temperate eels, although so very different from both the morphological and ethological points of view, offer the most striking analogies in their breeding habits :

(1) They become silvery at the adult stage and leave the freshwater for the sea : (In the speckled or marbled species, the silvering causes a uniformity in the dress.)

(2) They reproduce in the sea.

(3) From their eggs are hatched larvæ or leptocephali closely similar to the *brevirostris* leptocephalus. After 1925, thanks to

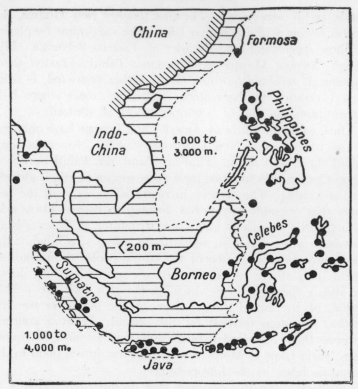

FIG. 55.   Eel distribution in South-East Asiatic seas.

Note their absence from coasts verging on the continental platform
(horizontally shaded); and the extension of the Japanese eel as
far as Tonkin (oblique shading) (*after Schmidt and Delsman*).

the material collected near the Celebes by the American expedition of the *Albatross*, Schmidt was able to identify larvæ and
semi-larvæ of the species *A. marmorata*. In 1930, at the start
of the world cruise of the *Dana*, the larvæ of several species
in the Indian Ocean were in their turn identified. Jespersen
(1942) was able finally to publish a complete study of these
leptocephali.

(4) After their metamorphosis, the young transparent eels
or elvers invade the continental waters and penetrate into the
freshwater. These ascents have been observed in Sumatra,
New Guinea, and elsewhere.

After all these similarities in habits, we are justified in supposing that the inter-tropical eels seek the depths and the warm
waters for spawning. Schmidt has recognised two of these
spawning grounds in the Indian Ocean : one to the east of
Madagascar, the other to the west of Sumatra (Montawei
deep). In the Pacific the spawning grounds seem to be more
numerous. Their multiplicity alone allows us to understand
that certain species, such as *A. marmorata* can be represented
by many distinct races on the neighbouring islands of Tahiti
and Samoa.

Let us examine in conclusion the curious case of the China
Sea. Between the depths of the Indian Ocean and Pacific
Oceans is a submarine plateau from which rise the Malay
Peninsula, Sumatra, Java and Borneo. The depth of water
over this Indo-Malayan plateau (Fig. 55) does not generally
exceed 200 metres, comparable with that of the North Sea.
But at the periphery they take a sudden plunge into the abyss
from 1000 to 3,000 metres. What is the result from the point
of view of the eel's distribution? A double inquiry made by
Schmidt (1925) and Delsman (1929) allows us to answer this
question. On the ' plateau ' aspects of these coasts there is a
total absence of eels. Neither the Malay Peninsula nor Indo-
China possess any of the species so abundantly represented on
the ' abyss ' side. An island such as Sumatra has eels in the
rivers of its south-west coast and none in those of the opposite
slope. In Borneo, it is the east coast, turned towards the deep
Straits of Macassar, which alone has any eels.

Thus, the inter-tropical eels combine with the necessity of
reproducing in deep water—a conclusion already expressed—
a total incapacity to accomplish extended larval migration.
Those hatched at the periphery of the Indo-Malayan plateau
are incapable of crossing it to populate the coasts. It is as if
the elvers of the European eel metamorphosed in the open sea
off the Anglo-Breton coasts and then found it impossible to invade the Channel and the North Sea.

A question of currents arises to complicate matters farther
north, where there exists, according to Chevey (1935), a north-
south current which runs along the South China coasts and an
opposite one which runs up those of the Philippines. The first

is cold and carries the temperate eel away from Japan towards Indo-China. The second is warm and carries away the equatorial eel *A. marmorata* as far as subtropical Formosa. The mixing of the waters due to these currents ought to favour the populating of the Indo-Malayan plateau with eels. Since it has no such result, one may conclude with all certainty: (1) that the inter-tropical eels spawn solely in the great depths situated in the immediate neighbourhood of the coasts where they accomplish their growth; (2) that they cannot, after starting from these spawning grounds, travel for long distances before and after their metamorphosis.

According to Jespersen (1942) in consequence of these facts, the larvæ of the inter-tropical eels, having a very short pelagic existence, have necessarily a very rapid growth (for instance 2–3 months for *A. bicolor* instead of the three years for *A. anguilla*). But as the rapid growth does not compensate for the brevity of the larval life, the leptocephali are smaller in size, at the moment of their metamorphosis, than those of the temperate eels. The absence of seasonal variations of temperature makes possible, on the other hand, an almost uninterrupted reproduction for inter-tropical eels. The final result of all these facts is that leptocephali of extremely diverse sizes can be captured in the same place. By these characters the inter-tropical eels contrast with the temperate eels which have, as we remember, remote spawning grounds and extensive migrations.

There has been, on the whole, " evolution by lengthening of the larval life " in proportion as the eels have left the tropical zone to spread out beyond the tropics and as far as the polar circle. Because their need of warmth at the time of spawning brings them back every year into the warm waters, it has been necessary for their larvæ to adapt themselves to longer and longer journeys. Of them all, the European eels hold the record. It was one of the outstanding achievements of Johannes Schmidt to know how to link its apparently singular biology with that of all other eels scattered throughout the world.

BIBLIOGRAPHY

CHEVEY, P. Sur la présence du genre *Anguilla* en Indochine française. *Bull. Mus.*, Series 2, Vol. 7, pp. 65–68, (Paris, 1936).
DELSMAN, H. C. The distribution of freshwater eels in Sumatra and Borneo. *Treubia*, Vol. 11, pp. 287–292, pl. 5, (Batavia, 1929).
EGE, V. A revision of the genus *Anguilla* Shaw. A systematic phylogenetic and geographical study. *Dana Report*, No. 16, (Copenhagen, 1939).
EKMAN, S. Prinzipielle über die Wanderungen und die tiergeographische Stellung des europäischen Aales. *Zoogeographica*, Vol. I, No. 2, pp. 85–106, (Jena, 1932).
GERMAIN, L., JOUBIN, L. and LE DANOIS, É. Une esquisse du passé de l'Atlantique Nord. *La Géographie*, Vol. XXXIX, pp. 281–293, (Paris, 1923).
JESPERSEN, P. Indo-Pacific leptocephalids of the genus *Anguilla*. Systematic and biological studies, *Dana Report*, (Copenhagen, 1942).
SCHMIDT, J. On the distribution of the freshwater eels throughout the world. I. Atlantic Ocean and adjacent regions. A biogeographical investigation. *Medd. Komm. Fisk.*, Vol. III, No. 7, pp. 1–45, (Copenhagen, 1909). *Idem.* II. Indo-Pacific region. *Mem. Ac. R. Sc. Lett. Denmark*, s. 8, t. 10, pp. 329–382, (Copenhagen, 1925).
Les anguilles de Tahiti. *La Nature*, t. 2, pp. 57–63, (Paris, 1927).
The freshwater eels of New Zealand. *Trans. N. Zealand Inst.*, Vol. 58, pp. 379–388, (Wellington, 1927).
The freshwater eels of Australia with some remarks on the short finned species of *Anguilla*. *Austr. Mus. Mag.*, Vol. 16, pp. 179–210, (Sydney, 1928).
SMITH, H. M. A review of the history and results of the attempts to acclimatize fish and other water animals in the Pacific States. *Bull. U.S. Fish Comm.* Vol. XCVI, pp. 379–472, (Washington, 1895).
ÜBISCH, L. V. Stimmen die Ergebnisse der Aalforschung mit Wegeners Theorie der Kontinentalverschiebungen überein? *Die Naturwissenschaften*, Vol. XXIV, No. 12, (Berlin, 1924).

N

Prof. Léon Bertin

The following obituary notice by Dr. E. Trewavas is reprinted by permission from Nature, *April 14, 1956.*

ON February 4, in his sixtieth year, Prof. Léon Bertin was killed in a motor-car accident on the frozen roads outside Paris. He had held the chair of herpetology and ichthyology at the Muséum National d'Histoire Naturelle since the death of Pellegrin in 1944.

Bertin graduated at the École Normale Supérieure of Paris in 1920 and was awarded a bursary to study for a doctorate. Under Prof. Bouvier he had been initiated, as he said, " au dur métier de la systématique " in the field of entomology, and he now took up the study of sticklebacks in a way that would have astonished Mr. Pickwick. Johannes Schmidt had just demonstrated the value of biometry in analysing the races of *Zoarces* and contrasting their diversity with the homogeneity of the populations of the European eel. Bertin applied like methods to sticklebacks and published on them a series of papers culminating in the classical " Recherches bionomiques, biométriques et systématiques sur les Épinoches (Gasterostéidés) " (1925), which won him his doctorate. The three-spined stickleback shows, in the amount of dermal ossification, a diversity which, expressed in the number of lateral shields, lends itself to numerical analysis. By examining ten thousand specimens from forty-five localities in France and North Africa, Bertin was able to correlate the degree of armature with age, salinity and latitude. Although later work by Heuts has shown that his conclusions were over-simplified, Bertin produced order from chaos and laid a firm foundation on which others have built. The French sticklebacks proved to have a life-span of fourteen to eighteen months. Later, Bertin studied large samples from Iceland and Greenland and demonstrated that these do not become sexually mature until their third or fourth summer, and that they thus conform to the rule of longer life-span in higher latitudes.

This work was followed by studies on bathypelagic eels and then on those enigmatic eel-like fishes, the Lyomeri. Bertin was entrusted with rare and precious material of these groups collected during the cruises of the *Dana*. As well as a number of smaller papers, he published three *Dana* Reports on them (the first in collaboration with Roule), and he had work on them in hand at the time of his death.

187

Throughout his career Bertin was associated with the University of Paris and the Museum. His courses at the University were much appreciated; he also developed a talent for popularization. The biggest work of this kind from his hand is "La Vie des Animaux" (1949–50). His contribution to the "Traité de Zoologie" is due to appear shortly.

Bertin served his country as a soldier in both World Wars, and received the Croix de Guerre for courage under bombardment in 1940. A man of distinguished appearance, his personality was dynamic and gay, and it is this that gives a special sadness to his sudden and tragic end. He leaves a widow and three children.

INDEX